**FEDERATION OF
Ontario Naturalists**

Plantwise

Pamela M. Hickman

Illustrations by Judie Shore

Kids Can Press Ltd.

Toronto

Kids Can Press Ltd. acknowledges with appreciation the assistance of the Canada Council and the Ontario Arts Council in the production of this book.

Canadian Cataloguing in Publication Data

Hickman, Pamela
    Plantwise

At head of title: Federation of Ontario Naturalists.
ISBN 1-55074-001-6 (bound)
ISBN 1-55074-044-X (pbk.)

1. Plants – Juvenile literature. 2. Plants – Identification – Juvenile literature. 3. Plants – Problems, exercises, etc. – Juvenile literature. 4. Plants – Identification – Problems, exercises, etc. – Juvenile literature. I. Shore, Judie. II. Federation of Ontario Naturalists. III. Title.

QK49.H52   1991   j581   C90-095461-2

Text copyright © 1991 by Pamela Hickman and the Federation of Ontario Naturalists
Illustrations copyright © 1991 by Judie Shore

Kids Can Press Ltd.
585½ Bloor Street West
Toronto, Ontario, Canada
M6G 1K5

Book design by Michael Solomon
Typeset by Compeer Typographic Services Limited
Printed and bound in Canada by John Deyell Company

91   0 9 8 7 6 5 4 3 2 1

Text stock contains over 50% recycled paper

CONTENTS

For my husband Doug who is
ever enthusiastic and
encouraging, and our children
Angela, Connie and Jenny who
make discovering nature even
more fun.
P.H.

For my mom and dad.
J.S.

Plant parts

Plants are everywhere — window sills, gardens, sidewalk cracks, farmers' fields, parks and even in water. Whether you live in the city or in the country, take a closer look at the plants around you and find out how they grow. Read on to discover what the different parts of plants do and how they make new plants. Then have fun growing crooked plants, finding exploding seeds, making leaf skeletons, and more.

Plant particulars

Hundreds of millions of years ago, plants appeared on earth. They're now the most widespread and numerous living things. Whether you like your plants big or small, nature's got something for you. From the giant west-coast redwoods reaching more than 105 m (345 feet) tall, to the microscopic algae in a pond, the world of plants offers an endless display of shapes and sizes. Even your own neighbourhood is home to a great variety of plants. Just look at the differences between the grass, trees, garden flowers, vegetables and houseplants growing around you.

Even though there are many different sizes and types of plants, all plants have the same basic parts. Just as your heart and lungs are major organs in your body that you couldn't live without, plants also have organs that they couldn't live without. The three essential parts that most plants have are roots, stem and leaves. The roots anchor the plant and take up water and minerals from the soil to the rest of the plant. The stem acts like a main highway system for the plant—it's the busy travel route for water and minerals going from roots to leaves and for food coming from leaves to the rest of the plant. The stem also supports the plant and is the place where all other plant parts are attached. The green leaf of a plant is a mini food factory for the plant (see box on page 7).

The flowering part of the plant is responsible for producing seeds that will, in turn, create new plants in the following season. The key to success in plants, as in all nature, is to continue producing generation after generation.

6

Mini food factory

Plants don't have to go out and hunt for food; they make their own food. The leaves of most plants act like mini food factories where they make food called carbohydrates, or sugars, for the rest of the plant. To make this food, leaves need three essential ingredients: water from the soil; carbon dioxide from the air; and energy from sunlight. This process of making food for the plant is called photosynthesis.

During photosynthesis, water is drawn into the plant through the roots and travels up the stem to the leaves. The carbon dioxide from the air enters the leaves through tiny pores called stomata. The stomata can open or close, depending on the amount of water available in the plant, so that if there is a lot of water present, the stomata open, allowing some water to escape while letting the carbon dioxide enter. With the final ingredient of sunlight, the process of making food can begin.

The chlorophyll, or green colouring, in leaves uses the sun's energy to start the chemical reaction that eventually produces carbohydrates and oxygen. The carbohydrates produced are carried to other parts of the plant in the liquid sap that flows through special tubes in the stem. The stored food is used to help the plant grow. The oxygen that is produced in the chemical reaction is released into the air through the stomata. Since water is not only an ingredient in photosynthesis, but also moves out of the leaves when the stomata are open during photosynthesis, a lot of water is necessary for the food factory to function.

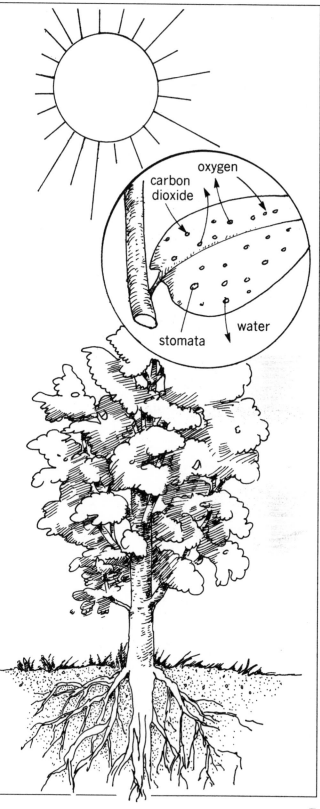

Searching for sun

You need nutritious food and water in order to stay healthy and grow. Plants also need food (minerals) and water, but another important ingredient is sunlight. This activity will help you see just how far a plant will go—or grow—in order to reach sunlight.

You'll need:
2 sheets of heavy black paper
a fast-growing plant, like a bean seedling
    planted in a pot
sticky tape
scissors
water

1. Roll one sheet of paper into a tube large enough to fit around the potted plant. Tape the sides together securely and set the roll of paper aside.
2. When your seedling is 3 to 4 cm (1 to 2 inches) high, place the tube of paper over the pot. Cut your tube so that it is a few centimetres (1 inch) higher than your plant.

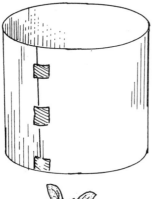

3. Cut a piece of black paper to make a lid that will lie flat over the top of your tube. Towards one edge of the lid, cut a hole about 2 cm (1 inch) wide as shown.

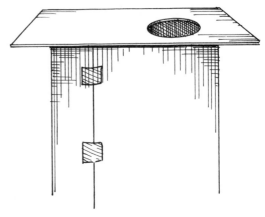

4. Place your plant, in its tube, in front of a bright window. Remember to water the plant.
5. The plant inside the tube will be growing in the dark. It will react to the small circle of light let in by the hole in the lid and will grow towards it. Once you see the plant poking through the hole, remove the black paper and look at the shape of your plant. You will find that the stem has grown long, spindly and crooked, stretching for the light.

What is a weed?

Ever wonder how a gardener knows which plants to pull up and which ones to leave growing in the flower bed or vegetable patch? It really just depends on who the gardener is. Some people consider anything that wasn't planted in the garden on purpose a weed. So, a pretty flower unlucky enough to spring up among the potatoes gets pulled up. Weeds are often unattractive, aggressive plants ready to overtake a garden if not stopped. A weed can be any plant that is simply growing where it is not wanted. The more tolerant the gardener is to surprises, the less weeding she has to do!

Bonsai

Have you ever seen a 100-year-old pine tree that's only 20 cm (8 inches) tall? If you visited a Japanese bonsai garden, that is what you'd see, along with many other tiny trees. Bonsai is the art of growing dwarf trees by carefully depriving them of nutrients, cutting back their fastest-growing shoots, clipping their roots and keeping them in small pots so that the root systems can't grow. The reward for all this work is a tree that grows into a miniature version of its regular self, but with twisted and sometimes interesting shaped trunks. Bonsai is an example of the fun you can have "playing" with plants.

Rooting around

If your family has lived in your neighbourhood for a long time, then they have "put down roots." This means that they have established themselves in the area and will probably stay there for many more years. The deeper the roots, the harder it is to leave. This expression of "putting down roots" comes from comparisons to the roots of plants. Plants with large, deep roots are well anchored in the soil and are likely to stay there for a long time. Plants with short or shallow roots are more easily blown over by wind or pulled up by animals. Why do the roots of some plants grow deeper than others? It sometimes depends on where the plant is growing. Roots growing in deep, rich soil can grow down farther than those growing in shallow soil. As well, a plant growing in a very wet area tends to have shallower roots than one that is growing in a dry area where the roots must search farther to find water.

There are two main kinds of roots: tap roots and fibrous roots. A plant with a tap root usually has a very thick, deep, main root with tiny roots growing off it. The thickened part of the root not only helps anchor the plant, but it is also used to store food that the plant has produced during photosynthesis (see box on page 7). A carrot is an example of a tap root. Oak, hickory and walnut trees also have tap roots. The food stored in the root is used to help the plant grow, especially in the spring before the plant has grown leaves and is able to photosynthesize again. Tap roots are also an excellent source of food for animals, including people. In fact, you've probably eaten many kinds of roots without even knowing it. Did you know that potatoes, turnips, beets, sweet potatoes, radishes, rutabagas and parsnips are all kinds of roots? Their high concentration of carbohydrates makes them a good source of food energy for people.

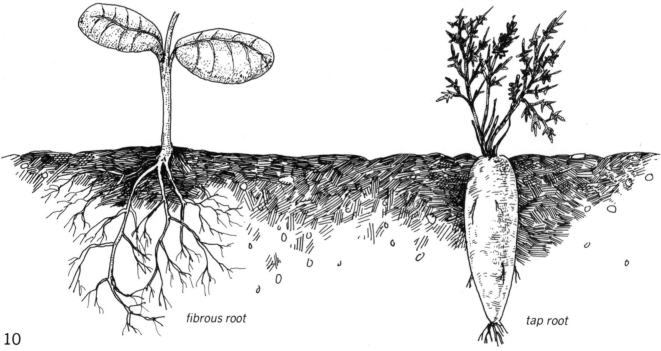

fibrous root

tap root

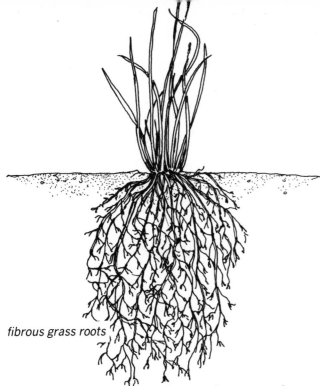

fibrous grass roots

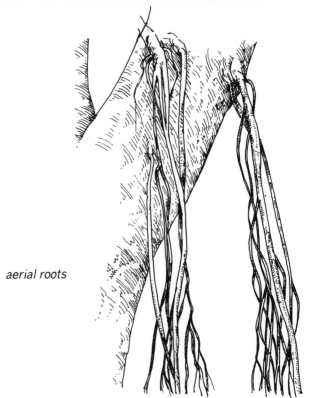

aerial roots

Fibrous roots are made up of a mass of finger-like or thread-like roots that spread out in the soil. Many garden plants, such as peas, and houseplants, such as geraniums, have fibrous roots.

Besides providing an anchor for plants, roots also have the job of absorbing water and minerals from the soil to feed the rest of the plant. To do this, some roots grow to incredible lengths. For example, the roots of a single rye plant can grow an average of 5 km (3 miles) a day under ideal conditions! The roots of one tuft of grass combined may total more than 600 km (400 miles) in length! It would be impossible to measure all the roots of a large tree, but generally, the growing root tips reach out in the soil just beyond the spread of the outermost branches. It's only the root tips that absorb the water and minerals from the soil so, if you're watering a tree in your garden, water it at a distance from the trunk, not close up. And don't skimp on the water—a mature birch tree's roots can absorb 4000 L (900 gallons) of water per day in the summer.

Likely most plants and trees that you've seen have tap roots or fibrous roots that grow undergound. But many trees in the cloud forests of the tropics sprout aerial roots from high up on their branches. These roots grow down until they reach the soil, probably helping the tree absorb more nutrients from the soil. Other trees have stilt roots that grow from the trunks and help anchor the trees in the soil.

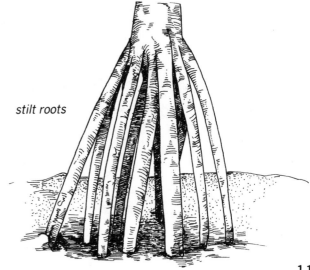

stilt roots

11

Putting down roots

How can you turn one plant into two or turn part of your lunch into a plant? It may sound like magic, but all you need to do is grow some roots. Try these simple tricks for rooting plants and you can expand your collection of houseplants in no time.

To root a cutting **you'll need**:
a sharp knife
a geranium
a flower pot
potting soil
water
a plastic bag
an elastic

1. Cut a 15 cm (6 inch) shoot (branch) from a geranium plant, near a joint where a leaf meets the stem.

2. Pull off the lowest couple of leaves. Plant the shoot in a pot of potting soil so that about half of the shoot is buried.

3. Water the soil and place a plastic bag over the pot and plant, to keep moisture in. Close the open end of the bag with an elastic.

4. Leave the plant in a shaded spot for two or three weeks. To check whether the roots have grown, gently tug on the stem. If the cutting doesn't slip out easily, then it has rooted.

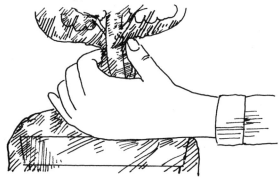

5. When the cutting has rooted, remove the plastic bag and keep the pot in the shade until the plant begins to grow well. Then transfer it to a sunny location.

Growing garbage

If you've eaten an avocado for lunch, instead of throwing out the huge pit inside, save it to start another avocado plant. You can grow carrot plants by cutting off and saving the top few centimetres (inch) of an unpeeled carrot. Or if you come across a potato that has already sprouted little white "eyes," put it aside and use it to grow a potato plant indoors.

You'll need:
an avocado pit, carrot top or sprouted
   potato
a glass
water
toothpicks
plant pots
potting soil

1. Any of the above plant parts can be rooted in the same way. Fill the jar with water.
2. Stick some toothpicks into the avocado pit, and rest it on the rim of the jar as shown. The bottom of the pit should be in water.

3. Place the jar on a window sill. Keep the water level high so that the lower part of the pit is always in water.
4. In a few weeks, you should see the pit split and a root emerge from the bottom. Shortly afterwards, a shoot (stem) will begin to grow upwards from the pit. When the plant sprouts its first leaves, remove the toothpicks and carefully transfer the pit to a pot containing soil. Be very careful not to disturb the root. Place your plant near a sunny window.

Growing with gravity

If you plant a seed or a bulb upside-down in the ground, will the roots grow up through the soil and the stem grow down underground? The answer is always no. No matter how you do your planting, the stem will always grow up and the roots will always grow down. How does the plant know which way is up? The plant is responding to the earth's gravitational pull—a reaction called geotropism. Gravity causes the plant's growth hormone, called auxin, to collect on the underside of the root and shoot. The root and shoot cells, however, react differently to the auxin. In the shoot, the auxin stimulates growth and causes the underside of the shoot to grow more rapidly, thus raising the shoot up. However, auxin has the reverse effect in the root. The auxin inhibits growth on the underside of the root, thus causing the top side to grow more rapidly, sending the root downwards.

What would happen if astronauts took plants up in space where there is no gravity? Experiments have shown that when gravity does not direct the growth of a plant, the roots and shoots will grow any which way.

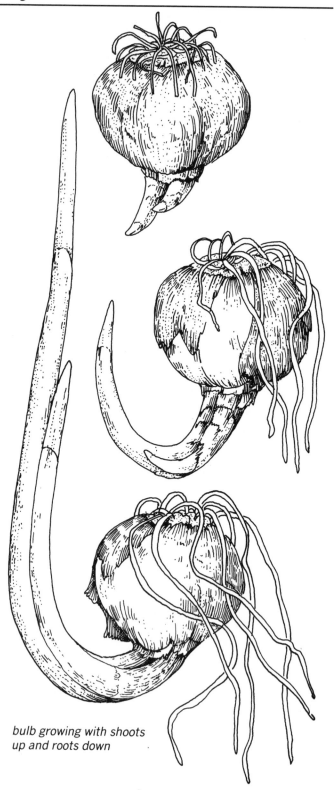

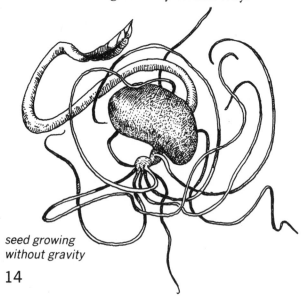

*seed growing
without gravity*

*bulb growing with shoots
up and roots down*

14

Plant pretzels

You can see geotropism in action for yourself by planting some radish seeds and turning them into wild-looking plants.

You'll need:
10 radish seeds
water
a glass jar
wet paper towels

1. Soak your radish seeds in water for a few hours.
2. Line your glass jar with wet paper towels.
3. Slide your seeds between the paper towels and the glass, so that you can see them.

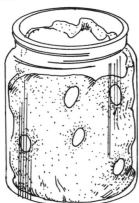

4. Put your jar in a dark cupboard until the seeds have sprouted and the stem is about 3 cm (1 inch) long.

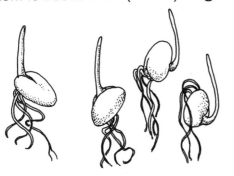

5. Pour off any extra water from the jar and turn the jar on its side. Keep the jar in the dark so that your stem's growth is not affected by the direction of light.

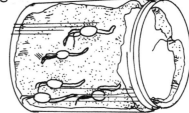

6. After one day, look at the roots and stems. In what direction are they growing?
7. Turn your jar right side up again and make sure the paper towels are still wet. Leave the jar in the dark for another day.

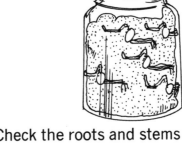

8. Check the roots and stems again. Are they still growing in the same direction or have they changed? You should find that no matter what position your jar is in, the stems will always grow up and the roots will always grow down. By changing the jar's position, you have made gravity turn the plant this way and that.

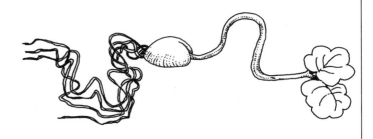

Looking at leaves

Your hand is like a leaf. Look at the underside of your wrist and notice all the veins running from your arm into your hand. Leaves also have veins that run from the branch into the leaves. The veins in your hand are covered by skin and tissue and are hard to see. Although a leaf's veins are covered by leaf tissue, their outlines are visible as ridges on the leaf. Your veins carry blood from your hand back to your heart. Plants don't have blood, of course, but they do have a watery liquid called sap in their veins. Inside the veins of a leaf are two sets of tubes. One set of tubes, called xylem (zi-lem), carries water and minerals from the roots into the leaves. The other set of tubes, called

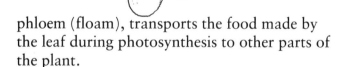

phloem (floam), transports the food made by the leaf during photosynthesis to other parts of the plant.

The veins also act like bones. They provide support to the leaf tissue, like your bones support your body's tissues. When there is a lot of water available to the plant, the veins are full of sap and the leaves are well supported. But if water is not available, the veins will lose their stiffness and the leaf will collapse, or wilt. To get a closer look at a leaf's veins and compare the vein patterns of different kinds of leaves, you can strip away the tissue and make leaf skeletons (see page 18).

Collecting leaves

Take a look at the leaves in your garden, in your local park or on your houseplants. What kinds of shapes do you see? There's an almost endless variety of plant leaves, and that makes looking at them and collecting them lots of fun. Here's an easy way to preserve the leaves in your collection.

You'll need:
a variety of leaf shapes
waxed paper
a dish towel
an iron (Ask an adult to help you.)
glue
several sheets of three-ring binder paper
a binder

1. Collect a sampling of undamaged leaves from a variety of plants. Try to find as many different shapes as possible (see page 21). You can collect green leaves in summer and coloured leaves in fall.

2. Fold a piece of waxed paper in half so that the waxy surface is on the inside. Make sure the folded paper is large enough to cover your biggest leaf.

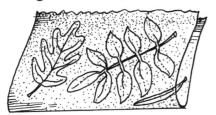

3. Place a leaf between the folded waxed paper. Cover the paper with a dish towel and carefully iron on top with a hot iron. The heat from the iron will melt the wax onto the leaf. This waxing process should prevent the leaf from drying out.

4. Glue each leaf to a sheet of paper. Beside the leaf, write where you found it, when, and what kind it is.

sugar maple

backyard October

5. Store your collection in a binder.

Making leaf skeletons

With some water and warm weather, you can get an undercover look at the leaves in your neighbourhood.

You'll need:
a variety of green leaves (maple, poplar, elm, basswood)
a dishpan
water
garden soil or compost (not sterilized soil)
old newspapers
a bowl
paper towels
paint (optional)
glue (optional)
heavy paper (optional)

1. Place the leaves flat in the bottom of your dishpan and cover them with water. Add some soil to the water. Bacteria in the soil will help the leaf tissue decompose.
2. Put newspapers on top to weigh down the leaves.

3. Leave the dishpan outside in a sunny spot for two to three weeks. The water-leaf mixture may begin to smell as the leaf tissue rots, so it is best to leave it undisturbed and away from the house.

4. Remove the newspapers and take out a few leaves at a time.
5. Place the leaves in a bowl of warm water and very gently rub them between your thumb and forefinger. This should remove the remaining leaf tissue and expose the veins.

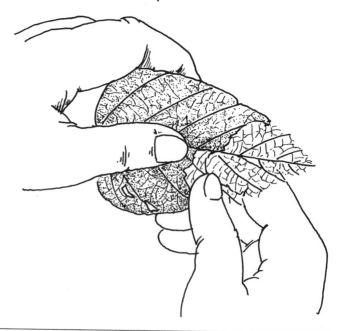

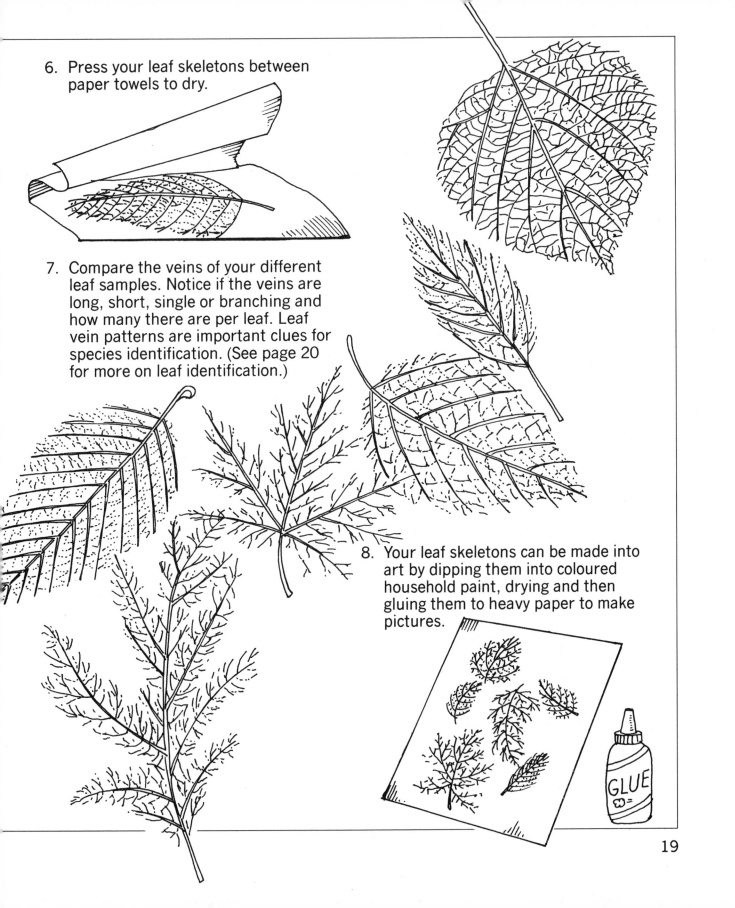

6. Press your leaf skeletons between paper towels to dry.

7. Compare the veins of your different leaf samples. Notice if the veins are long, short, single or branching and how many there are per leaf. Leaf vein patterns are important clues for species identification. (See page 20 for more on leaf identification.)

8. Your leaf skeletons can be made into art by dipping them into coloured household paint, drying and then gluing them to heavy paper to make pictures.

GLUE

Identifying leaves

The arrangement of leaves on a plant and what the leaf itself looks like are very important clues for plant identification. Once you have had a good look at a leaf, check a field guide (see page 96) to help you identify the plant. Many field guides to trees or wildflowers have easy-to-use keys for plant identification. A key asks you a series of questions about what your plant looks like, including various details about leaves. When you have answered all the questions, the key will identify your plant.

Here are some of the characteristics field guides use to describe leaves. How many of these types of leaves have you seen?

1. Check to see how the leaves are arranged on the plant.

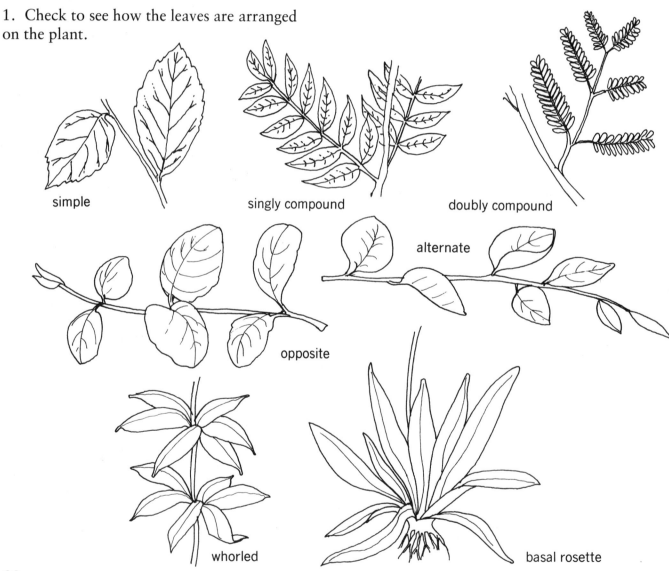

simple

singly compound

doubly compound

alternate

opposite

whorled

basal rosette

2. Notice the shape and texture of the leaf.

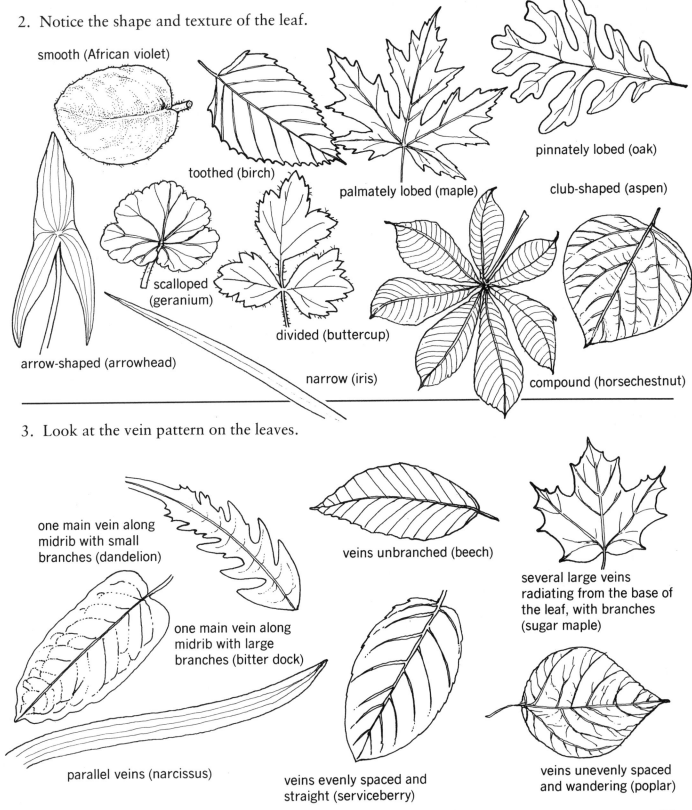

smooth (African violet)

toothed (birch)

palmately lobed (maple)

pinnately lobed (oak)

club-shaped (aspen)

scalloped (geranium)

divided (buttercup)

arrow-shaped (arrowhead)

narrow (iris)

compound (horsechestnut)

3. Look at the vein pattern on the leaves.

one main vein along midrib with small branches (dandelion)

veins unbranched (beech)

one main vein along midrib with large branches (bitter dock)

several large veins radiating from the base of the leaf, with branches (sugar maple)

parallel veins (narcissus)

veins evenly spaced and straight (serviceberry)

veins unevenly spaced and wandering (poplar)

21

Falling for autumn

If you live where there are cold winters, you know that a sure sign that winter's coming is the colour change of the leaves on the trees. Why do leaves suddenly change colour? In most cases, the new colours, such as orange and yellow, have actually been in the leaves throughout the year, but they were hidden by the dominant green colour of chlorophyll. Some colours, though, such as reds, aren't produced until the fall. In the fall, the tree prepares for a rest. It will not grow during the winter because of the cold temperatures and lack of water. Part of the tree's preparation for winter involves stopping photosynthesis. First the chlorophyll in the leaves breaks down and when the green colouring breaks down, the other colours can be seen.

Once the leaf colours have brightened up the landscape, it will soon be time to get out the rake as the leaves begin to fall. Only certain types of trees, called deciduous, shed all their leaves at once. Oaks, maples, poplars and hickories are all deciduous trees. Where you live, the annual dropping of leaves likely occurs in the cool days of autumn. But even in tropical areas or climates with wet and dry seasons, deciduous trees lose their leaves at the start of the dry season.

Why do trees get rid of their leaves? The main reason is to conserve water. In cold winters, for example, the ground is frozen and it is very difficult for the roots to soak up water. So the tree has to stop using as much water as possible. Since leaves use up and release a lot of water, especially during photosynthesis, the leaves have to go. As autumn approaches, cells at the base of each leaf's stem die and form a barrier that blocks the flow of food and water between the leaf and the tree. This, along with the breakdown of chlorophyll in the leaf, kills the leaf. Once the chlorophyll is gone, the leaf can't photosynthesize any more. Eventually, the leaf can't hold on to the twig any longer and falls to the ground. The tree remains inactive through the winter until spring, when the buds open and the new leaves grow and start to photosynthesize again.

Uncovering colours

Each year the trees treat us to a show of the beautiful oranges and yellows of autumn leaves. You can uncover the hidden colours in green leaves with this simple version of paper chromatography that helps you separate the different pigments (colours) in a leaf.

You'll need:
a few green leaves
a glass jar
rubbing alcohol
a metal spoon
a 4 cm x 9 cm (2 inch x 4 inch) strip of
    coffee filter paper
sticky tape
a pencil
a piece of plain white paper

1. Tear your leaves into tiny pieces and put them in the jar.
2. Cover the leaves with rubbing alcohol. Caution: This liquid is poisonous, so do not taste it and avoid inhaling the fumes. Ask an adult to help you.
3. Mash the leaves up with the spoon and leave the mixture for 5 minutes.

4. Lower one end of the filter strip into the jar so that it just reaches the liquid inside. Tape the other end to your pencil and lay the pencil across the open jar mouth as shown.

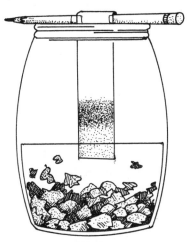

5. Watch as the liquid moves up the filter strip. When it is about half-way up, remove the strip and lay it on some clean paper to dry.
6. When the filter strip is dry, notice the bands of colour on it. You should see a green band, left by the chlorophyll pigment and a yellow or orange band left by a pigment called a carotenoid. The rubbing alcohol separated the pigments from the leaf mixture, and the filter paper absorbed both pigments and rubbing alcohol.
7. Try the same activity with leaves that have already turned colour.

How does it work?
The pigments, or colours, of the leaves were dissolved in the solution and then reabsorbed onto the filter paper. Since each pigment travelled on the paper at a different rate, each dried at a different location along the strip of paper. The result is a series of coloured bands, each representing one of the leaf's pigments.

Flower finery

If you visited a florist or walked through a rose garden, you might be tempted to think that flowers exist to fill the air with perfume and the landscape with beauty. Although people do get a great deal of pleasure from looking at flowers, they don't bloom for us. A flower's sole purpose is to get pollinated and produce seeds for a new generation of plants. Pollination involves the union of a pollen grain from the male organ of a flower with an egg inside the female organ of a flower. Once united, they form a seed.

One of the main pollinators of flowers is bees. Imagine if you could shrink down to bee-size and buzz your way right into the centre of a flower. Before you reached the nectar treat you were searching for, you'd first have to manoeuvre past a number of other flower parts. Already covered with yellow, dust-like pollen from the last flower you visited, your back would brush against the stigma of the female organ and leave behind some pollen to pollinate the flower. Next you'd wind past the male anthers that would sprinkle even more pollen on your hairy body. You will probably carry this new pollen to another flower and pollinate it too. Eventually you'll descend deep inside the flower cup where your long journey will be rewarded by a drink of sweet nectar.

Flowers use pretty colours and scents to attract pollinators. Since different pollinators are attracted to different things, you can often tell what pollinates a flower by the way the flower looks or by what time of year it's in bloom. Take a look at how the plants on these pages attract pollinators.

Methods of Pollination

Location of flowers on plant

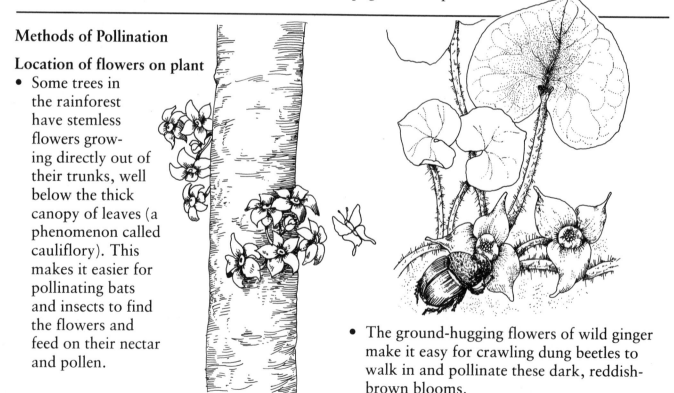

- Some trees in the rainforest have stemless flowers growing directly out of their trunks, well below the thick canopy of leaves (a phenomenon called cauliflory). This makes it easier for pollinating bats and insects to find the flowers and feed on their nectar and pollen.

- The ground-hugging flowers of wild ginger make it easy for crawling dung beetles to walk in and pollinate these dark, reddish-brown blooms.

Colour of flowers

- Flowers pollinated by birds, mainly hummingbirds, are usually red or orange. Each large, showy bloom will provide a long sip of nectar for the bird, but will not give out enough nectar to fill the bird up. This encourages the bird to visit more flowers in order to satisfy its appetite. At each visit, the bird picks up pollen on its head, face, chest or bill and rubs it off onto the next plant.
- Stripes or patterns on the petals of some flowers, such as common wood-sorrel, guide the pollinator to the source of nectar and past the pollen-laden anthers.
- Many pollinating insects are very sensitive to ultraviolet light, although people cannot see it. Flowers such as dandelions reflect ultraviolet light and therefore stand out like a beacon to an insect flying over an otherwise grey-looking field.

Scent of flowers

- Not all flowers have a pleasant scent, but they still manage to attract pollinators. Flies, naturally attracted to the odours of rotting meat, are lured by the foul-smelling flowers of skunk cabbage and red trillium.

- Wafts of scent grab the attention of insects flying by a basswood tree or field of thistles. Although perfume often means a sweet reward of nectar, this is not so for early-blooming orchids. The beautiful colour and sweet scent of some lady's-slippers, rose pogonia and others, invite hungry bees to "step inside" the flower. The structure of the flower forces the bee to rub past the pollen-producing anthers on its way out, but there is no nectar to be found.

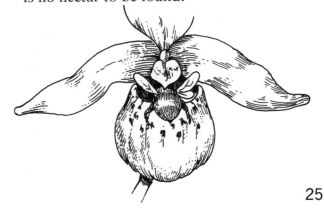

25

Shape of flowers

- Wide open, flat flower surfaces, like those of bloodroot, make great landing pads and touring sites for insect pollinators, such as beetles, that like to crawl around.

- A group of small orchids has flowers that look, at first glance, like an insect sitting on a flower. There is a fly, a spider and a bee orchid. The imaginary insect attracts male insects that try to mate with the "female" on the flower, while at the same time pollinating the orchid.

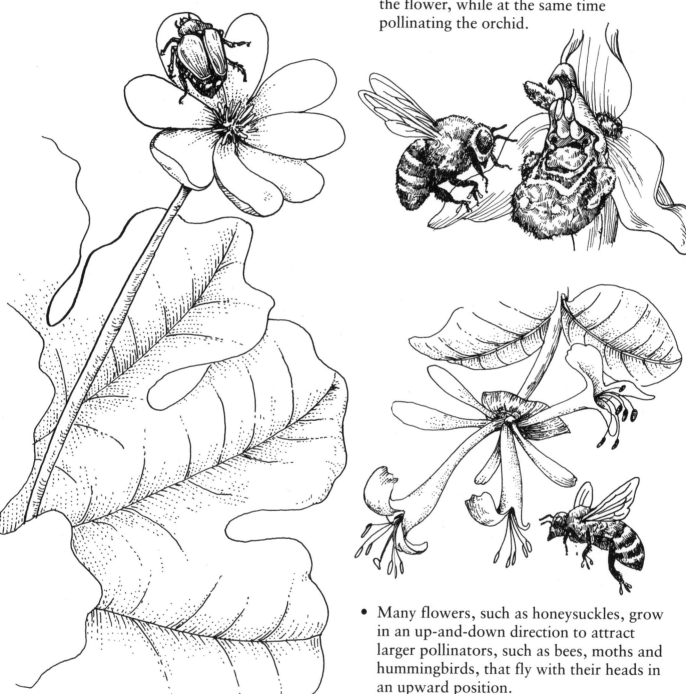

- Many flowers, such as honeysuckles, grow in an up-and-down direction to attract larger pollinators, such as bees, moths and hummingbirds, that fly with their heads in an upward position.

Timing of blooms

- The time of blooming is very important for flowers. The earliest bloomers in spring, like leatherwood and crocuses, attract hungry insects without having to compete with fields of other flowers. Fall bloomers, such as goldenrod and asters, also benefit from less competition.

Types of flowers

There are two basic types of flowers: regular and irregular. The petals of a regular flower are arranged around the central organs. Each petal is the same size, shape and colour as the others. Most flowers, including lilies, roses, buttercups and asters are regular flowers. In an irregular flower, petals are not similar in size, shape or colour. Instead, the flowers may have upper and lower parts called lips that look quite different from each other. Violets, orchids and peas are examples of irregular flowers.

A single flower may appear on a stem, like a tulip, or there may be a large cluster of tiny flowers packed together to form one large flower-like head, as seen in clover.

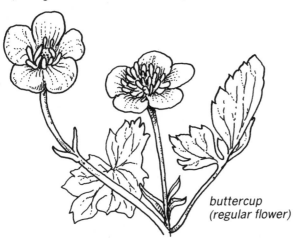

buttercup
(regular flower)

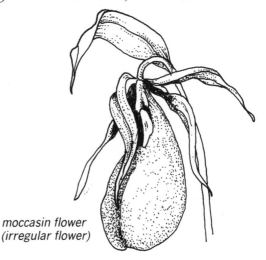

moccasin flower
(irregular flower)

Dissecting a flower

Try dissecting a flower to get a look at the parts inside.

wild geranium

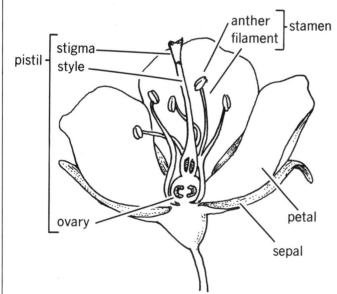

You'll need:

a single, regular flower in full bloom (tulip, Easter lily, tiger lily for example)

1. You'll see six petal-like parts. The three outside parts are the sepals. (On some flowers these will look like green leaves.) The sepals protect the flower when it is in the bud stage. Gently pull the sepals off.

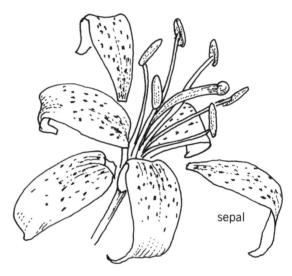

2. Next, look at the petals. Their colour, shape or size is probably designed to attract pollinators, but the petals also protect the sex organs of the flower from drying out.

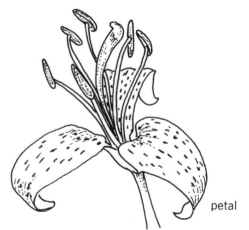

3. Take off the petals and look for the stamens—the flower's male organs. They look like thin stalks, called filaments, with club-like heads. The heads are called anthers and are usually yellow, but may be other colours, including black in the tulip. Gently touch an anther with your finger. If it is ripe, a yellow (usually) dust-like substance, called pollen, will rub off onto your finger. Try to see where the base of the stamen is attached.

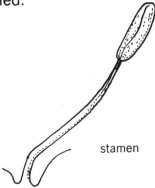

stamen

4. Pick off the stamens, leaving the central pistil, or female organ. The pistil has three parts: a swollen base, called the ovary, where the seeds form; a stalk-like style; and an enlarged head, called a stigma, where the pollen must land in order to fertilize the flower. Try to find all these parts.

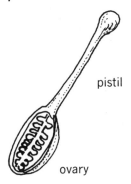

pistil

ovary

5. Different flowers will vary in their structure. Some have many separate pistils, for example, while others may have no styles. The basic parts, however, should still be visible. When you're admiring the flowers in your house, garden or neighbourhood park, take a moment to see if you can find the different parts in various flowers.

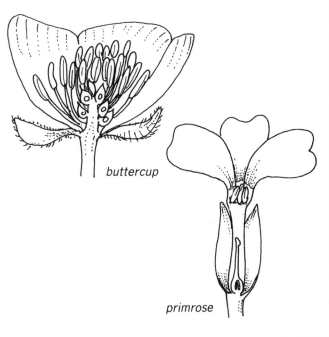

iris

buttercup

primrose

Sowing seeds

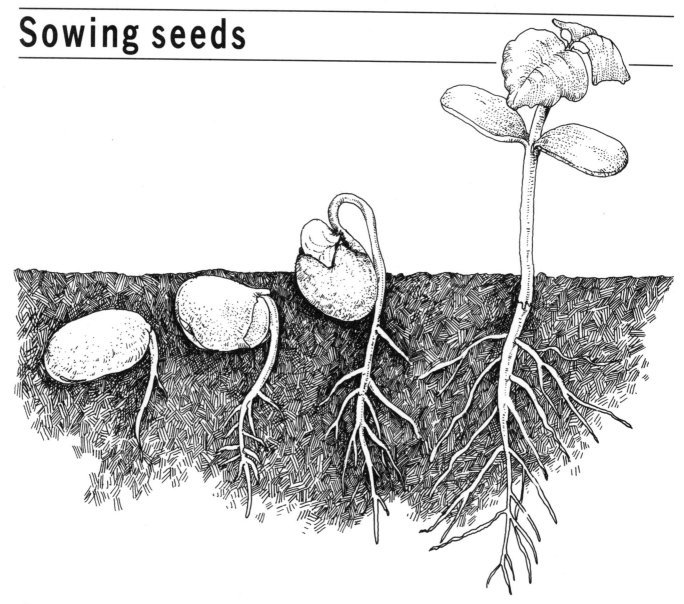

If you've ever planted seeds, you know how exciting it is when you see the first signs that your plants are growing. You may notice a little bump in the soil and then some cracking of the soil surface. The tiny shoot from your seed is pushing its way up through the soil to reach the open air and sunlight. Have you ever wondered how your seeds have the strength to move soil or what happens after you plant the seed to turn it into a growing plant?

Like a sponge, your seed soaks up water. As the water is absorbed, the contents of the seed swell and swell until they crack the seed coat (outer shell of the seed). Inside the seed, the root and shoot cells have stretched with all the water they've soaked up, and they are now free to grow out from the seed coat and push through the soil. This process is called germination. As the cells stretch and multiply, the plant parts are pushed further and further through the soil until you see the shoot poking up into the air.

Bursting beans

Find out how mung beans turn into mighty beans and blow their cork as they germinate.

You'll need:
a clear plastic jar with a cork stopper (available at craft stores)
fresh mung beans (available in grocery stores)
water
a plastic bag
a twist tie

1. Fill the jar with mung beans and add water until it reaches the top of the beans.
2. Put the cork firmly in the mouth of the jar.
3. Place the jar in a plastic bag tied with a twist tie and put the bag in a dark cupboard for 3 to 4 days.
4. Check the jar. You should find that the cork has been pushed out of the jar by the pressure of the growing beans inside.
5. Notice the level of water in the jar now. The beans have absorbed the water and swelled. Inside each bean, the root and shoot cells have taken in water and started to stretch. It is these stretching cells that eventually burst from the seed and push through soil.

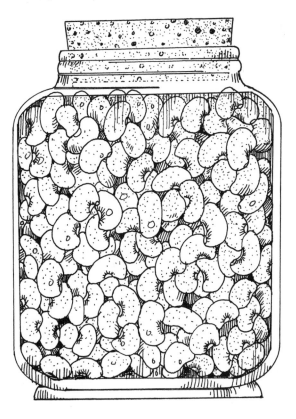

So long, seeds

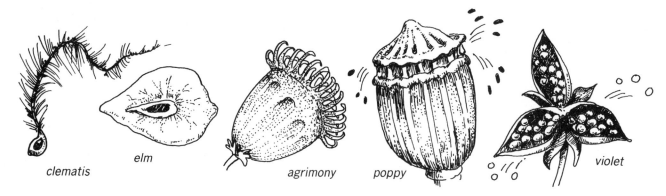

clematis   elm   agrimony   poppy   violet

What do parachuting, hitch-hiking and exploding have to do with seeds? They're all different ways that plants send their seeds off to find a new place to grow. Why is "transportation" so important for seeds? Since plants depend on water, soil, nutrients and light in order to grow, the more plants there are in one area, the greater the competition for these resources. By dispersing its seeds, a plant helps prevent over-crowding and over-use of the nutrient supply. Dispersal also helps plants colonize new areas and helps ensure that all the seeds will not be wiped out if a "disaster" occurs in one area. Because a seed can't control where it will land, the majority of seeds do not end up in a place suitable for germination. Therefore, a plant may produce an enormous quantity of seeds to improve its chance for successful reproduction. For instance, one orchid seed pod can contain up to 3 million seeds! Read on to find out how some seeds glide, ride and catapult to a new home.

Parachuting seeds

Have you ever picked the white fluffy seed head of a dandelion and blown on it? The small brown seeds are attached to a long stalk with a wisp of fluff at the top. Your blow, or a gentle breeze, sends the feather-light seeds floating away in the air. Eventually they will descend here and there like parachutes. Other parachuters include fireweed, goat's-beard and common milkweed. Some wind-blown seeds, such as maples, ashes and some conifers, have "wings" that glide them through the air, sometimes carrying the seeds a very long way.

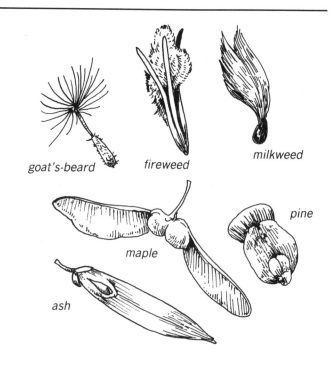

goat's-beard   fireweed   milkweed   maple   pine   ash

Animal gardeners

If you've ever had to brush burs out of your pet's fur or pick tick-trefoil seeds off your sweater, you know how well the seeds' tiny hooks and barbs can cling to fur and clothing. These seeds are especially designed to hitch-hike on passing wildlife, or people, to get a free ride through the woods, across a field or as far as they can get.

Wildlife also play an important role in seed dispersal through their eating habits. Many birds and other animals eat berries (which contain seeds) but can digest only the fleshy part of the fruit. What happens to the seeds? They come out in the animal's waste, often a long way from where the berries were picked. Some animals, especially squirrels, act as nature's gardeners. They bury seeds, such as walnuts and chestnuts, for future food supplies but sometimes fail to return to eat them.

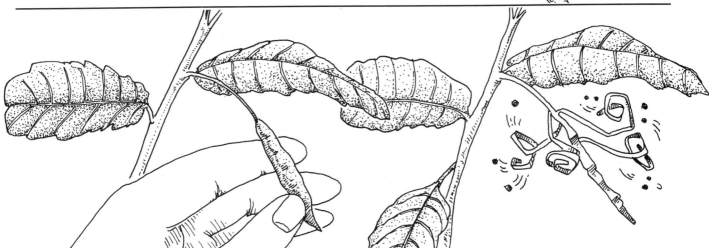

Seed explosions

Some seeds explode into the air when ripe or shoot out of their protective pods at the slightest touch. Jewelweed is a great example of an exploder that is fun to play with. Look for the orange, spotted, trumpet-like flowers of jewelweed in damp areas such as marshes, swamps or along the edges of streams. If you find a plump, dry seed pod hanging from the plant, gently squeeze it between your thumb and forefinger. Almost instantly, the pod will separate into pieces and roll up, shooting out the seeds in all directions. Growing by flowing water can also be an advantage to jewelweed since some of its seeds can be carried downstream and deposited on a new shore.

Socking it to seeds

You can get a great collection of seeds by letting your feet do all the work. Here's how.

You'll need:
a pair of old wool socks
tweezers
glue
heavy paper
labels
a pen
clear pill bottles with lids

1. Put the old wool socks on over your shoes and take a walk through a field in late summer or early fall.

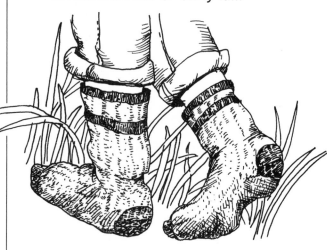

2. You'll find that a variety of seeds will be picked up by the socks. At the end of your walk, take your socks off and use tweezers to pick off the seeds.

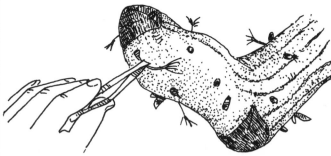

3. Try to separate the seeds by size, shape or colour. How many different kinds did you get? What is the most common seed in your collection? What might this tell you about the plants growing in the field?

4. You can try the same activity in a forest or across a backyard and compare the number and variety of seeds you get.

5. To display your collection, you can glue your seeds in groups to heavy paper. Your collection may represent the seeds of your backyard or neighbourhood, a particular habitat such as a field, or the seeds may be sorted by shape, size, colour, or method of dispersal (see page 32). Each group of seeds should be labelled, saying when and where it was found.

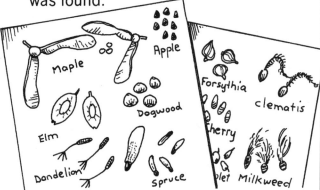

6. You may want to keep some of your seeds in pill bottles over the winter and plant them the following spring to see what kind of plants they grow into. Store these seeds in an unheated place or in the refrigerator to simulate the natural cold that seeds endure during winter outdoors.

Investigating plants

Even though plants can't talk, they can still tell us a lot about what's happening around them. For example, holes drilled into a tree trunk can let you know that a woodpecker has been there. Thorns, prickles or itchy juices tell people and wildlife to stay away. In this section you'll find out what the plants in your neighbourhood are trying to tell you, and you'll discover other fascinating plant facts. For instance, have you ever wondered what happens to plants in winter?

Winter wonders

Did you know that some plants hibernate in the winter, just as some animals do? When you get the winter blues and you're longing for a breath of spring, you can get a sneak preview of the spring to come by searching for April's flowers below the snow.

You'll need:
a trowel
a field guide to wildflowers
a pencil
paper

1. Visit a wood lot where you've seen spring flowers blooming in past years. If you can remember just where certain flowers bloomed, that'll make it easier. If not, look for open spaces away from tree trunks.
2. If the snow is deep, use your trowel to clear a patch of forest floor. With your hands, gently brush away the fallen leaves and look for the leaves of over-wintering wildflowers. These are flowers whose stems have died back to the ground, but whose roots and, sometimes, basal leaves are still alive. Instead of starting out from seed in the spring, the plant will grow from its hibernating roots. Some flowers may appear as a ring of green leaves hugging the ground, while others may show the remains of last year's dead leaves through which the new season's growth will appear.
3. Look for wild ginger, hepatica, bloodroot and others. You may need your field guide to identify the plants.
4. Cover the "sleeping" flowers back up with the leaves and snow to keep them protected from the cold.
5. Make a note of where you found flowers by sketching a small map. Return in the spring to see what has bloomed. If you record the locations of spring wildflowers in bloom, you can find them much more easily next winter.

Nature's antifreeze

If trees are 80 to 90% water, do they freeze solid in cold winters? The answer is yes, but it doesn't hurt the trees. As the cold weather approaches, the concentration of sugar in the tree's cells increases, acting as a sort of antifreeze. However, the sugar concentration is not enough to stop the trees from freezing solid during the coldest parts of winter. In the early spring, when the nights are freezing and days are milder, the higher sugar concentration in the sap causes the sap to thaw by day, although it may still freeze at night. It is this alternate freezing and thawing within the tree that forces the sap to flow. Try this simple activity to see how sugar helps lower the freezing temperature of water.

You'll need:
2 plastic cups
water
sugar
a spoon
a freezer

1. Fill each cup half full of water.
2. To one cup, add 2 heaping spoonfuls of sugar. Stir until the sugar is dissolved.

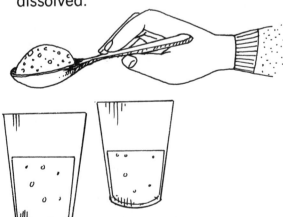

3. Place both cups in a freezer. After an hour, compare the contents of each container. You should find that the sugar-water mixture has not frozen solid, while the cup of pure water contains solid ice. Eventually, the sugar-water will freeze too because of the very cold temperature of your freezer.

How does it work?
The sugar in the water acts as an antifreeze, lowering the freezing point of the water. Therefore, the pure water will freeze solid more quickly and at a higher temperature than the sugar-water. If you could set your freezer temperature to 0°C (32°F) (the freezing point of water), you would find that the pure water would be frozen, while the sugar-water would not be frozen solid.

Sweet sap

If you like to dig into a pile of pancakes dripping with pure maple syrup, try making your own syrup. Once the weather has turned to warm days and cold nights in the early spring, you should be ready for action. Nature has already made the sugar-sweet sap inside the maple trees — all you have to do is get it out, cook it and eat it up.

You'll need:
a hand drill with an 11 mm (7/16 inch)
  drill bit
mature sugar maple trees
spiles (available at most hardware
  stores)
pails (large plastic ice-cream pails work
  well) with plastic bags for lids
string
a large pail or container
a large pot
a stove
Mason jars with lids
a sharp knife
small sticks
a hammer

1. Drill one or two holes in each maple tree at about waist height. If two holes are made in the same tree, drill them on opposite sides of the tree. An average tree will produce about 55 L (12 gallons) of sap over a three-week sap run. You'll need to collect a lot of sap — it takes about 180 L (40 gallons) of sap to make 5 L (1 gallon) of syrup.

2. Insert the spiles into the holes and hang the pails from the spiles. Tie a plastic bag over each pail and spile with string to help keep dirt and bugs out of your sap.

3. Collect the sap in your large container at least once a day.
4. Pour the sap into a large pot that you keep on simmer on your stove. As long as steam is rising from the pot, the water is evaporating from the sap and making it thicker. The pot must never boil dry, so keep adding sap as the level in the pot goes down.

5. As the sap thickens, it will turn from an almost colourless, watery liquid into an amber-coloured, concentrated syrup. Once you think it has reached the right taste and consistency, pour it into jars and seal them.

6. You can also make chewy maple taffy by pouring some hot syrup in a cup of clean snow. In a few seconds, you'll have a sweet, tasty candy to eat.

7. When the sap is finished running, or you've collected enough, remove the pails and spiles from the trees. Ask an adult to whittle a sharp point on one end of a small stick and hammer the stick into the hole left by the spile. This acts like a bandage for the tree.

Plant protectors

With the swing of an axe, snip of the scissors or stomp of your foot, you have the ability to kill or injure almost any plant—big or small. How can plants defend themselves from powerful people like you? A number of plants have special adaptations that help protect them from people, other animals or other plants.

Some of the plant protectors are easy to see, while others are well hidden. Without you even knowing it, plant protectors may be working against you in your own backyard. Take a look at how these plants defend themselves.

Stinging nettle leaves have hollow needles attached to venom-filled sacs. When the needles touch your skin, they break and squirt out venom, causing a painful sting and mark on your skin.

Black walnuts spread a poison through the soil around their roots to keep other plants from growing and competing with the tree.

The thorns on rose bushes don't stop you from smelling or admiring the pretty flowers, but they do keep you from picking them.

If you like to climb trees, stay clear of this hawthorn with its long, needle-like thorns.

"Leaves three, leave them be" is an old saying about poison ivy. The sap from poison ivy can cause a very itchy rash on your skin.

Weeding the flower bed is usually not a problem, until you come across a prickly thistle. Even gardening gloves don't stop the prickles from getting into your hands. People often just leave the thistles alone.

41

Climbers and clingers

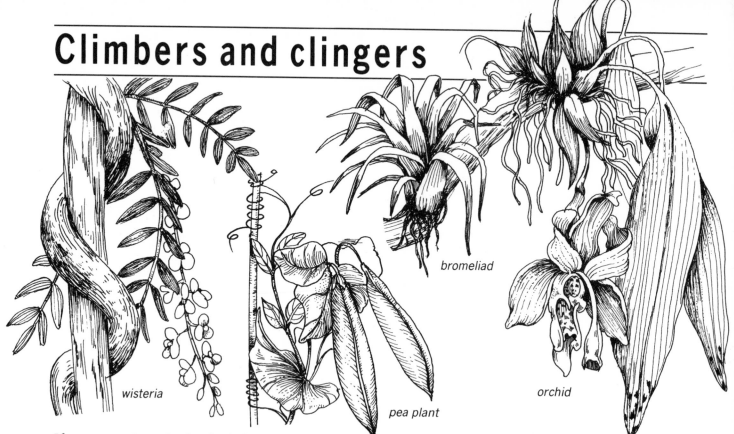

wisteria

pea plant

bromeliad

orchid

If you were in a thick, dark forest and wanted to see the sun overhead, what would you do? You could climb a tree. That's what plants called lianas do. Various vines and ivies use trees as stepladders to the sun. Some, like wisteria, climb by twisting their stems around and around a tree trunk, climbing higher at each turn. The stems of some climbing rattans can be up to 200 m (650 feet) long!

Passion flowers and pea plants use tendrils—modified stems or leaf stalks—to coil themselves around a support and pull themselves up, while the familiar climbing rose uses its thorns to hook into a supporting tree. Since climbers are rooted in the ground, they can get their own food and water and rely on their host tree trunk or other plant for climbing support only.

Plants known as epiphytes, sometimes called air plants, are another group of sun seekers. Instead of climbing trees, they actually germinate and live high up in tree branches. Many mosses, ferns, orchids, bromeliads, lichens and liverworts are examples of epiphytes. But how do these high-rise dwellers get food and water when their roots are nowhere near the ground? Rain is their main source of water. Some plants, such as orchids, absorb and store rain water in special organs such as swollen stems, while the flared leaves of bromeliads can capture and store water in their central "cup."

The nest fern has an amazing way of getting food. Its large leaves form a basket-like rosette, which collects smaller leaves as they fall from the host's branches above. Eventually, the collected leaves decay into a rich soil called humus that provides nutrients to the plant. The crotches of tree trunks and crevices of bark also provide potential humus storage sites for a variety of epiphytes clinging to a place in the sun.

Grow a plant pet

Add something new and different to your houseplant collection—grow a rabbit or an owl. It's amazing what you'll get when you combine an imagination with a green thumb!

You'll need:
a coat hanger
pliers
wire mesh
fine wire
wire cutters
a 25 cm (10 inch) flower pot
potting soil
3 ivy houseplants (such as English ivy)
twist ties
scissors

1. Ask an adult to help you straighten out the coat hanger with pliers. Bend the wire into the shape of an animal, leaving a small stem at the bottom for planting in the soil as shown.
2. Lay the wire mesh across your form and tie it on with the fine wire. Trim off any extra mesh around the edges of your form.
3. Fill the flower pot with potting soil. Plant the form securely in the pot.
4. Plant your 3 ivy plants at the base of the form and water as usual.

5. When your plants are about 25 cm (10 inches) high, tie them snugly to the form with twist ties, but don't damage the stems.
6. As the plants grow, train them along the form with twist ties. Clip off and remove any leaves that don't conform to the shape.
7. After 3 to 6 months, you should have a new plant pet.

Mistletoe vampires

Kissing under the mistletoe is a well-known tradition at Christmas, but did you know that these romantic plants are really killer parasites? Parasite plants live off other plants, sometimes killing their host plant. Mistletoes are examples of parasites that grow in temperate and tropical areas. Like epiphytes, mistletoe germinates and lives on the branches of trees and shrubs. But, instead of collecting its own water and

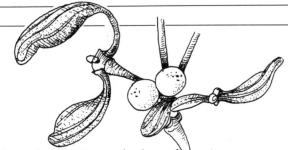

mineral salts, it steals these from its supporting host. With root-like structures resembling fangs, the mistletoe taps into the host's "plumbing" system and takes water and nutrients from it, sometimes draining its host to death.

Drink up

When you take up a drink through a straw, your sucking action pulls the liquid up the straw and causes more liquid to flow into the bottom of the straw. Plants also drink through a straw-like system of tubes, called xylem, inside their stems. The thin columns of water rise partly through a phenomenon called capillary action, in which water tends to "stick" together and rise. In addition, the leaves of a plant help to suck up the water by opening their stomata. When water reaches the leaves, most of it escapes through the stomata. The escaping water creates a suction, pulling water up the xylem tubes and causing more water to enter below at the roots. In this way, the column of water remains continuous, like the liquid in your straw. Only when you stop sucking, or you run out of juice, does the straw become empty. In large trees, the water may have to rise more than 30 m (100 feet). Not only does it go a long way, but it also flows very quickly, reaching speeds of 45 m (150 feet) per hour in some trees! To see how water is transported inside a plant, try the Plant Straws activity on the next page.

Plant straws

You can see for yourself how a plant draws water by giving it a drink of a different colour. Here's how.

You'll need:
a sharp knife
a fresh carrot with leaves
3 glasses of water
food colouring (red or blue)
a fresh celery stick with leaves
a white tulip or carnation

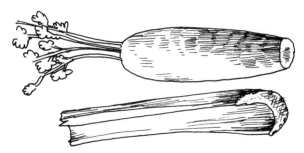

1. Cut the tip off the carrot and place the carrot into a glass of water. Add a few drops of food colouring to the water.
2. Place a celery stick in a glass of coloured water.
3. Place a white tulip or carnation in a glass of coloured water.

4. Leave all your glasses for several hours.
5. When you return, notice the colouring of the leaves and flowers. You will see that they have taken on some of the colour from the water.

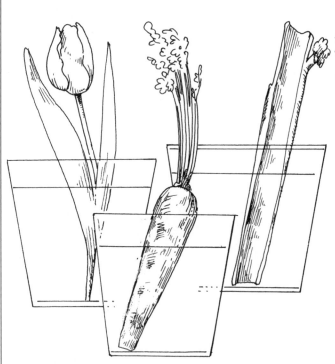

6. Carefully cut the carrot in two lengthwise and look at the core. Remember, the carrot is the root of the plant. The coloured core shows you how the root has drawn water up from the glass and passed it on to the stems and leaves.

7. Cut a slice from your celery stick. Notice the semi-circle of coloured dots. These are the ends of the xylem tubes that carried the coloured water up the stem of the celery plant. Gently scrape away the outer layer of tissue on the back of the celery stalk so you can see the coloured tubes.

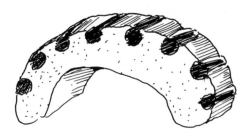

Sweaty trees?

When you're hot, your body sweats in order to help cool you down. Trees also sweat, but not to cool off. It's their way of getting rid of too much water. Except in very dry periods, leaves continually lose water through tiny holes called stomata. This loss of water is called transpiration. As water is lost from the leaves, it creates a sort of vacuum in the xylem. This draws more water up from the roots below. Although the plants absorb some of the water they draw up, most of the water is released back into the air. With some simple materials, you can see transpiration in action by capturing some of the water lost from a plant indoors or outdoors.

You'll need:
a plastic bag
a plant (not one with thick or waxy leaves)
string
water

1. In the morning (sunny days are best), put a plastic bag over a healthy leaf and tie the bag tightly shut with string. Be sure not to damage the leaf stem. If you're using a houseplant, make sure it is well watered.
2. Check your bag at the end of the day. You should see water droplets inside, caused by the plant's transpiration.

Trees are plants too

Trees are some of the biggest and oldest plants on earth. Trees can be living diaries of years gone by — they can tell us about past weather conditions, fires and droughts — and they provide homes for many animals. Join the tree team and learn how to measure the height of the tallest tree in your neighbourhood, hike a tree with your fingers and find out how dead trees turn into rich soil for new generations of plants and animals.

Tree totalling

If you grew like most trees do, the older you became, the fatter you'd grow. A tree trunk grows in width each year in a microscopically thin layer called the cambium. Towards the outside of the tree, the cambium produces phloem (floam) cells under the bark. These cells carry food up and down the tree until they die and form part of the bark. On the inside of the tree, the cambium divides into xylem cells that pipe water and minerals to the leaves, store food and form the support of the tree. In the spring or wet season, the growing conditions are usually best and large cells are produced, forming a wide, light-coloured ring of relatively soft wood inside the tree. In the summer or dry season, however, smaller, more condensed, thick-walled cells are formed, creating a dark ring of harder wood. The combination of one light and one dark ring represents one year's growth.

When a tree trunk is cut across its diameter, you can easily see the fresh rings. By starting at the centre and counting each pair of light and dark rings, you can tell how old the tree is. How old is the tree illustrated here? (Answer on page 96.)

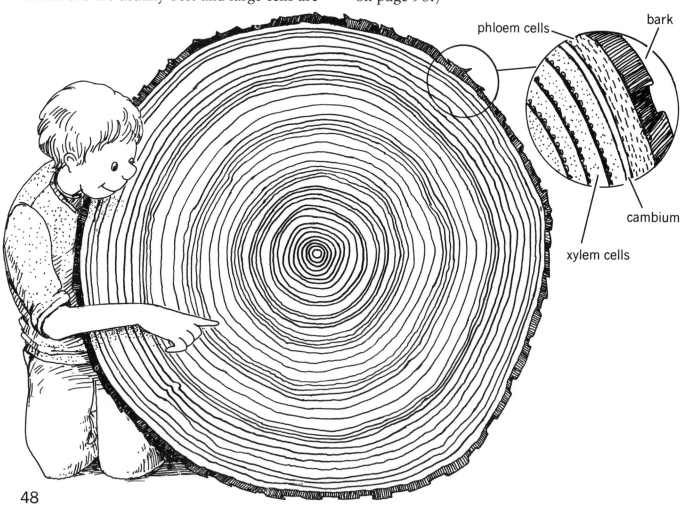

phloem cells

bark

cambium

xylem cells

Diary of a tree

You can find out more than just a tree's age from looking at its rings; you can also see what kind of life it's had.

Depending on the width of a ring, you can tell whether or not it was a good year for growth. For example, a very narrow, light-coloured ring may indicate that the tree suffered from a drought or too much shading from other trees for proper growth. Fire scars can be visible as charred areas, and signs of insect damage or disease may also be present. Sugar maple trees that have been tapped through the years may show the scars where the spiles were inserted. It's like reading a tree's diary of past events.

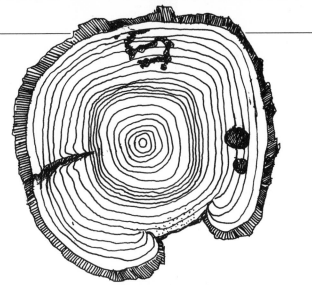

Branching out

Instead of looking on the inside of a pine tree to estimate how old it is, you can do it from the outside. Each year a pine tree adds a new whorl, or circle of branches, around its trunk. You can count the number of whorls to figure out how old the tree is. How old do you think this pine tree is? Turn to page 96 to see if you are right.

How high is up?

Trees are the tallest of all living things, and the Californian redwood is the tallest species of plant alive. Its record height is more than 63 times the height of the average person. If you want to find out the height of the tallest trees in your neighbourhood, try these two simple measuring tricks with the help of a friend.

Eyeballing it

You'll need:
a friend
a measuring stick
a pencil
paper

1. Stand facing the tree you want to measure. Hold your arm straight out in front of you so that your fist is level with your eye. Ask a friend to measure and record the distance between your eye and your fist (distance 1 on the diagram).
2. Hold a measuring stick straight up and down in your hand so that the distance from your hand to the top of the stick equals distance 1. (This is labelled 2 on the diagram; distance 1 = distance 2.)
3. Keeping your arm outstretched and your fist at eye level, walk backwards from the tree. Stop when the base of the tree lines up with the top of your fist and the highest twig of the tree lines up with the top of your stick.
4. Ask a friend to measure the distance between you and the tree trunk (labelled distance 3 on the diagram). This distance equals the height of your tree.

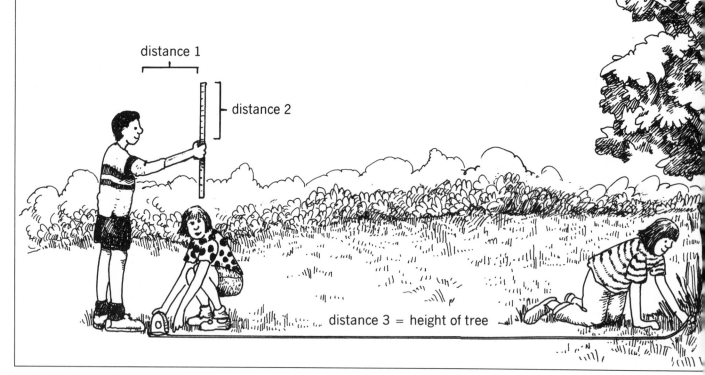

distance 1

distance 2

distance 3 = height of tree

Casting Shadows

You'll need:
a measuring stick or tape
a pencil
paper
a friend

1. On a sunny day, find a tree in an open area where its shadow is visible on the ground.
2. Measure and record your friend's height.
3. Have your friend stand near the tree, so that his shadow falls alongside the tree's shadow. Measure and record the length of your friend's shadow and the tree's shadow. Make sure all your measurements are in the same units (e.g., all in metres or centimetres).
4. Calculate the tree's height using this formula:

$$\text{tree's height} = \frac{\text{length of tree's shadow} \times \text{friend's height}}{\text{length of friend's shadow}}$$

Check the example below to see if you're doing your calculations correctly.

$$\text{tree's height} = \frac{\overset{\text{tree's shadow}}{(20\text{ m})} \times \overset{\text{friend's height}}{(1.5\text{ m})}}{\text{friend's shadow (3 m)}}$$

$$\text{tree's height} = \frac{30\text{ m}}{3\text{ m}}$$

$$\text{tree's height} = 10\text{ m}$$

Bark basics

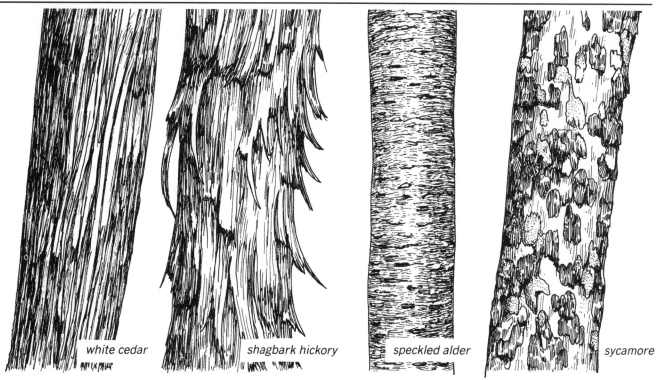

white cedar   shagbark hickory   speckled alder   sycamore

Imagine having armour two feet thick to protect you from injury! That's what a giant sequoia tree growing in California has. Its thick, tough layer of bark helps prevent damage to the wood beneath. A tree can't simply run from danger like you can, so it is shielded by its outer covering of bark. Not all bark is as thick as a giant sequoia's, though. A birch tree may have only 5 mm (1/4 inch) of protection.

Have you ever noticed how some trees have bark that's full of cracks and ridges while others have bark that seems to be peeling off in strips or patches? This happens when the growing tree trunk outgrows its bark "armour." The outer layers of bark—the cork layers—are dead. Since they can't grow any more, they split or peel off as the inner layers continue to expand and push outward. Trees never stop growing, although their rate of growth will vary depending on the weather and other growing conditions.

How wide will a tree grow? One of the thickest trunks known belongs to the African baobab tree. It can measure up to 54 m (180 feet) around!

52

A real corker!

Did you know that the cork on a bulletin board or in a wine bottle is actually made from the bark of a tree? Cork oak trees grow near the Mediterranean and have been harvested for more than 2000 years. Cork is used for a wide variety of products from baseballs and fishing-rod handles to flooring and insulation.

How is the cork gathered? It's sort of like shearing a sheep. The outer covering is harvested leaving the tree itself unharmed. The thick, spongy outer layer of bark is stripped from the tree during the summer with special axes and curved saws. The inner bark is left intact to continue to protect the tree and to form more cork. Unlike sheep, however, the trees can be stripped only every 8 to 10 years. Since cork oaks live for about 150 years, one tree

can produce a lot of cork. The stripped cork is stacked and left to dry for a few weeks before it is steamed or boiled, cleaned and prepared for shipping.

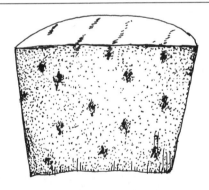

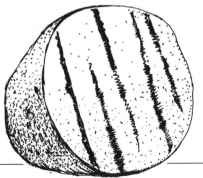

A cork up close

By taking a closer look at a bottle cork, you can see the signs of its origin as part of a tree.

You'll need:
a sharp knife
a bottle cork

1. Ask an adult to slice the cork in half, lengthwise.
2. Can you see the layers of cork, laid down as the tree trunk expanded each year?
3. You will also see tiny pores, called lenticels, that travel through the cork. These pores allowed air and water to move between the inner wood and the bark.

53

Hike a tree

Nature is like a big trunk full of interesting treasures. You may start out looking for one particular thing and before you know it, you've spent hours examining all of the other contents of the trunk. You may even forget what you started to look for! When you set out to look at a tree's bark or leaves, you can end up discovering amazing things about the insects, spiders, birds and other animals that live in or on the tree. To get a close-up look at your favourite tree and see how it's used by others, take a tree hike.

You'll need:
a magnifying glass
a trowel

1. Explore your tree from the ground up. Use your trowel to gently dig around the base of the tree. You may get a look at some of the tree's surface roots and, if you're lucky, you'll uncover some root-feeding insects such as cicada nymphs. Loose bark near the base of the tree is also a good hiding place for spiders and cocoons.

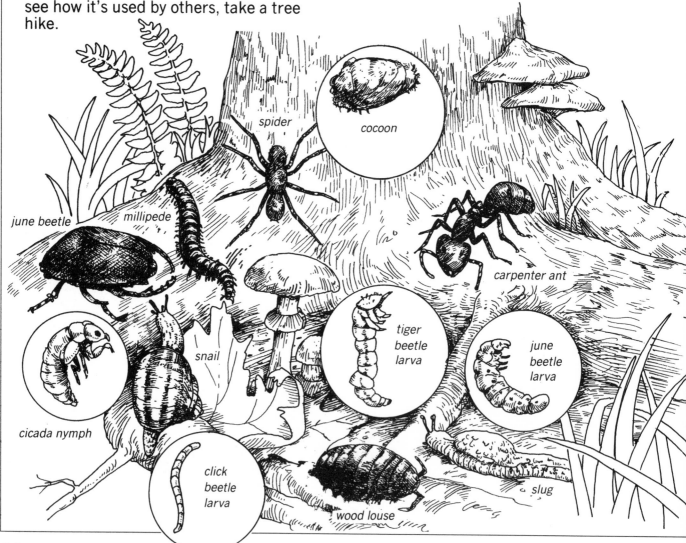

spider

cocoon

june beetle

millipede

carpenter ant

cicada nymph

snail

tiger beetle larva

june beetle larva

click beetle larva

wood louse

slug

2. Scan the cracks and crevices of the bark for insects and other invertebrates. Some spiders make tube-shaped webs on bark, while engraver beetles and carpenter ants leave entrance holes. And speaking of holes, check for the tell-tale signs of woodpeckers and sapsuckers. You may find mosses and lichens growing on the bark.

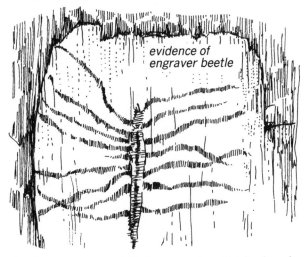

evidence of engraver beetle

3. Leaves provide homes to all kinds of creatures. Look for knobby growths caused by insect galls or fungi. Tiny transparent tunnels across a leaf are the signs of leaf miners. Unroll any cigar-shaped leaves to see if the young insects are still at home.

4. Look up. Are there any nests up in the branches? You may also see caches of food left by squirrels or birds in the crotches of large branches.

5. Depending on the time of year, you can check out the tree's buds, flowers or cones, too.

Coniferous trees

Did you know that the biggest and oldest living things on earth are conifers—cone-bearing trees? Among the world's 570 species of conifers, you'll find these super-trees:

- The tallest plants in the world are the coastal redwood trees of the Pacific Coast of North America. They can be more than 100 m (325 feet) tall—that's longer than a football field.
- The most massive trees are the giant sequoias of California. In fact, one giant sequoia in California, named the General Sherman, is 83 m (275 feet) tall, and measures more than 24 m (80 feet) around its trunk. It contains enough wood to build a village of 50 six-room houses!
- The oldest trees in the world are bristlecone pines of the Rocky Mountains in the southern United States; they can live to be more than 4600 years old.

All conifers don't grow to be as big and old as these, but they all bear cones, and most have needle-like leaves that help them withstand severe climates. The needles are compact, thick-walled and covered with a hard, waxy layer to reduce water loss. Inside the needles are resins that can quickly seal wounds to stop water leakage. You can sometimes feel this sticky resin when you touch the needles of coniferous trees. With these special adaptations, conifers can keep their leaves throughout the winter without losing too much water, unlike deciduous trees, which must lose their leaves in order to conserve water during the winter. Although some needles are shed every year, they usually stay on the tree until the new needles are fully grown, so you don't notice the change.

sequoia cone

bristlecone pine

sequoia

redwood

Coniferous and deciduous trees

Can you pick out the deciduous and coniferous trees in your neighbourhood? It's easy to find deciduous trees, such as maples, poplars and oaks, because most shed their leaves in the autumn or before a dry season. They also produce flowers, although you may not have noticed the flowers on some trees since they are so tiny. Coniferous trees produce cones instead of flowers. Most conifers are evergreen, which means that they keep their needle-like or

scale-like leaves all year round. Look for conifers such as pine, spruce, fir or cedar trees around your home.

Fungus friends

The next time you walk through a coniferous forest, try to notice how it's different from a deciduous forest. You may notice that there is not much growing beneath the trees and that there is a thick carpet of undecomposed needles on the forest floor. The soils in a coniferous forest contain high levels of acid, which doesn't attract many decomposing insects, bacteria, earthworms or other small animals. Where does this acid come from? The thick needles decompose very slowly and when they're attacked by fungi, a chemical reaction occurs, producing acids. As rain washes the acids down through the soil, it also carries away large amounts of minerals from the subsoil below. This leaves a thick, sterile soil layer where very few tree roots or other plants can grow.

So, how do conifers grow in such poor soils? The key to their success is a group of fungi known as mycorrhizae. Much of a conifer's roots may be surrounded by these fungus friends that collect nourishment for the tree. In return, the fungus gets carbohydrates from the root to help it grow and reproduce. Now, that's teamwork!

Cones

Can you imagine what the world looked like 300 million years ago? One thing you may be able to picture is the trees. That's when cone-bearing trees, such as pine and spruce, developed. Although it was such a long time ago, these trees, called conifers, haven't changed much over the years. In fact, conifers are some of the most successful plants in the world. They can grow in very cold or dry areas like the Arctic or desert edge where other plants can't survive. Much of their success is due to their cones.

The hard scales on the outside of the cone help protect the seeds inside from bad weather, poor growing conditions and cone eaters. When the right time comes, the scales can open and release the seeds to the wind, giving them the best chance of survival.

Pining for cones

Take a look at a pine tree in the spring. The reddish-purple cones growing upright at the tips of the branches are the young female cones. Now find the small, soft yellowish male cones farther down the branches. The yellow, dust-like pollen is blown by the wind from the male to the female cones. Once the female cone has been pollinated, its scales harden and close over the developing seeds. The cone stalk starts to bend downwards and the cone turns green. By the time the seeds inside the cone are ripe, the cone has turned brown and is pointing down towards the ground. At this time, the cone scales shrink and open, releasing the winged seeds to the wind.

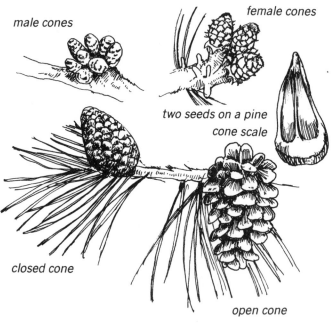

male cones

female cones

two seeds on a pine cone scale

closed cone

open cone

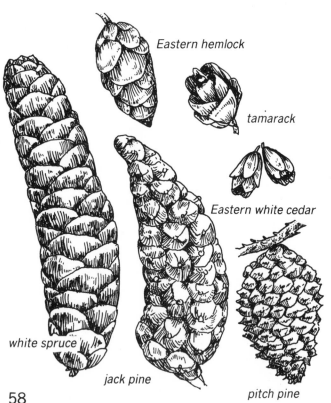

Eastern hemlock

tamarack

Eastern white cedar

white spruce

jack pine

pitch pine

In many kinds of conifers, the female cones form and ripen in the same year, but in pines it may take two or three years. You may be able to find cones at different stages of development on the same tree.

Cone magic

Conifer trees have survived so long because their cones are specially designed to open and close in order to protect or disperse their seeds at the right time.

You can make different cones open or close, like magic, by simulating the conditions that cones endure in nature.

You'll need:
5 jack pine or Scotch pine cones
a cookie sheet
an oven
2 dry, white pine or hemlock cones with open scales
a large bowl of water
a paper towel

1. Place one jack pine or Scotch pine cone on a cookie sheet and put it into an oven at 150°C (300°F) for 15 minutes. (Ask an adult to help you.) At the same time, place a cone of the same kind on a table for comparison.

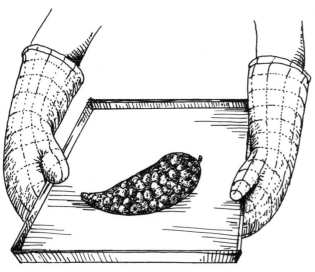

2. Check what has happened to the cone in the oven. Compare it to the cone on the table.

3. Try placing the other jack pine or Scotch pine cones in the oven, one at a time, at cooler or warmer temperatures to see what happens. You should find that a hot oven will make the cone open, releasing the seeds inside. The heat from the oven is doing what a forest fire in nature does. After a fire, jack pine seeds are released to the soil, where they can grow in the rich ashes of the burned wood, without any competition from larger trees. This helps them get a head start on other plants and helps the forest recover from the fire faster.

4. Place a white pine or hemlock cone in a bowl of water for 15 minutes. Leave the other cone dry for comparison.

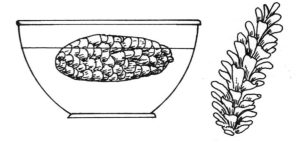

5. Check what has happened to the wet cone. You should find that the scales have started to close. The bowl of water represents a heavy rainstorm that could soak the cones. Since the seeds rely on wind to blow them to a new spot to grow, the seeds must be as light and dry as possible. In order to keep them dry, the scales close over the seeds during wet periods, acting like little umbrellas.

6. Take the wet cone out of the water and set it aside on a paper towel to dry. Watch what happens as the cone dries out.

Deciduous trees

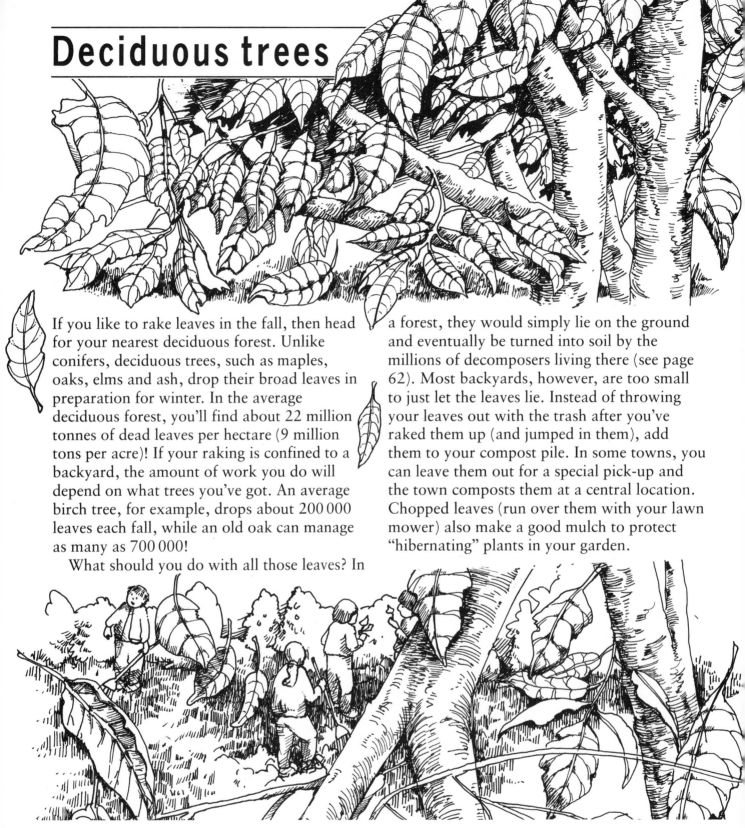

If you like to rake leaves in the fall, then head for your nearest deciduous forest. Unlike conifers, deciduous trees, such as maples, oaks, elms and ash, drop their broad leaves in preparation for winter. In the average deciduous forest, you'll find about 22 million tonnes of dead leaves per hectare (9 million tons per acre)! If your raking is confined to a backyard, the amount of work you do will depend on what trees you've got. An average birch tree, for example, drops about 200 000 leaves each fall, while an old oak can manage as many as 700 000!

What should you do with all those leaves? In a forest, they would simply lie on the ground and eventually be turned into soil by the millions of decomposers living there (see page 62). Most backyards, however, are too small to just let the leaves lie. Instead of throwing your leaves out with the trash after you've raked them up (and jumped in them), add them to your compost pile. In some towns, you can leave them out for a special pick-up and the town composts them at a central location. Chopped leaves (run over them with your lawn mower) also make a good mulch to protect "hibernating" plants in your garden.

Holey leaves

Despite what you may think, deciduous trees don't lose their leaves just to give you a job to do in the fall. The leaves are shed to help stop water loss through their stomata during winter. Since the ground is frozen, the tree cannot drink up any new water, even though it still gives off some water through its trunks and branches during winter. As long as the water loss isn't too severe, the tree will survive until spring.

Although the stomata are too tiny to see at a glance, try this trick to find out where they are.

You'll need:
a stove
water
a pot
a glass jar
some green leaves from a deciduous tree
(maple, birch, elm, etc.)

1. Boil some water in a pot and pour it into the jar. (Ask an adult to help you.)
2. Dip a leaf into the water.
3. Watch to see what part of the leaf the bubbles are coming from. The heat from the water causes the air inside the leaf to expand and pass out of the leaf through the stomata. If most of your bubbles are coming from the lower surface of the leaf, this means that most of the stomata are located there.

Real rotters

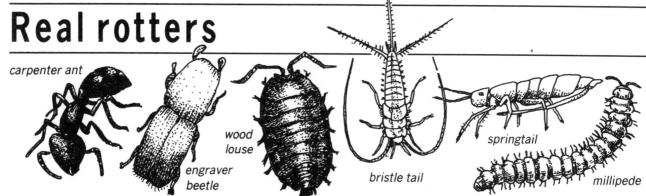

carpenter ant

engraver beetle

wood louse

bristle tail

springtail

millipede

Have you ever taken a walk through the woods after a big wind storm? Chances are you'll see a few trees that have been blown down onto the forest floor. What happens to dead trees? Sometimes they're cut up for firewood, but if they're left alone, they begin a whole new cycle. In fact, the death of a tree means the beginning of life for an entire community of insects, molluscs, amphibians, fungi, lichen and much more.

A freshly fallen tree can turn into a spongy-wood shelter for forest creatures and eventually becomes part of the rich humus on the forest floor. It's all due to the rotters—plants and animals that recycle wood by breaking it down into more simple forms that can be reused by other growing plants. The first of the rotters are the fungi. They settle on the tree, sending kilometres (miles) of hyphae (root-like strands) throughout the wood in only a few days. After the fungi have softened up the wood, a parade of invaders marches in, including bacteria (too small to be seen), insects such as engraver beetles, carpenter ants,

springtails and bristletails, wood lice, centipedes and millipedes.

If you were a small insect eater looking for food and shelter, what more could you want than a rotting tree or log? Toads, moles, shrews, salamanders, snakes and skinks are just some of the creatures that are attracted to the activity in a rotting log. When the tree has been "worked on" by the decomposers for several years, it may develop large hollow spaces inside. These spaces provide shelter for much larger animals such as skunks, raccoons, chipmunks, porcupines, martens or ermine.

A fallen tree can also provide a head start for other trees. Yellow birch and hemlock seedlings, for instance, have a hard time growing up through the thick layer of leaf litter on the forest floor. By rooting on top of and through a fallen tree, they get a boost up off the ground. This makes getting started much easier. So from the death of one tree springs the life of another and a whole community of fungi, insects, amphibians and animals.

Some plants up close

If you thought all plants were the same, then you're in for a surprise. In the next pages you'll discover some plants that have no flowers, no roots and not even stems. You'll also find out how some plants can grow in very dry areas while others flourish under water or eat insects to survive. And after you've read about grasses, you'll have a lot more to think about the next time you mow your lawn.

Fun with ferns

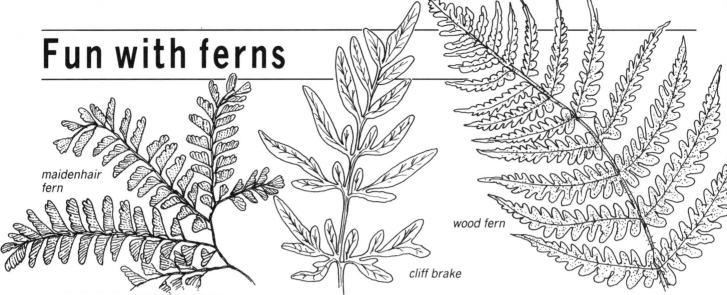

maidenhair fern

cliff brake

wood fern

If you have houseplants, you're probably living with some kind of fern, but did you know that wild ferns range in size from 1 cm (1/4 inch) long water plants to tree ferns reaching up to 20 m (65 feet) high? If there were a Hall of Fame for plants, ferns would be a star attraction. Not only were ferns the first plants to have roots, stems and leaves, but ferns and their relatives were the main land plants 350 million years ago. There are more than 10 000 kinds of ferns found around the world from the tropics to the Arctic Circle. They can grow in the ground, on trees or float in water. Some ferns live for centuries, although the individual fronds (leaves) usually last only about one year.

Fiddleheads

Have you ever gathered fiddleheads for supper in spring? For many people, fiddleheads are a great treat and they even provide a source of income for people who pick, process or freshly pack fiddleheads for markets around the world. What are fiddleheads? They're the new shoots of fern fronds, tightly coiled like the head of a violin. This is the stage at which they are picked for eating. As the frond grows, it stretches up and appears to lean backwards. By summertime, the frond and its leaflets have gradually uncoiled into a full frond. The fiddleheads of the ostrich fern are the most commonly harvested variety.

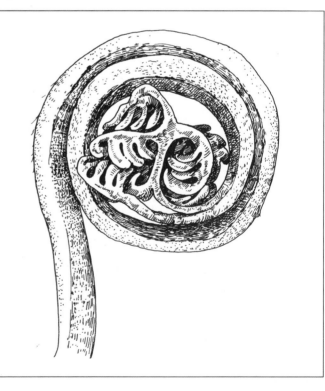

Scores of spores

Like mushrooms, ferns reproduce by microscopic spores. When a fern is three to seven years old, spores form in tiny spore cases, often on the backs of the fern's fronds. When they're ripe, the spore cases burst, releasing the dust-like spores to the wind. A single plant may produce as many as 50 million spores in one season. Some can travel as far as 15 000 km (10 000 miles) away from the parent plant.

You can search for spores on different ferns. The colour of the spore cases, shape and location of the spores are important clues to a fern's identity.

You'll need:
different ferns
a magnifying glass
a field guide to ferns

1. The spore cases are often arranged in tiny, dot-like masses, called fruit-dots. Use your magnifying glass to check the underside of the fern frond for fruit-dots. What colour are they? They should be either yellow, orange or brown.

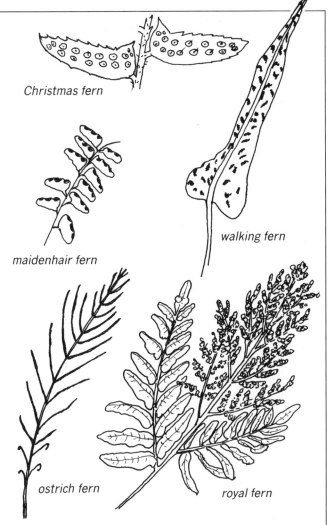

Christmas fern

maidenhair fern

walking fern

ostrich fern

royal fern

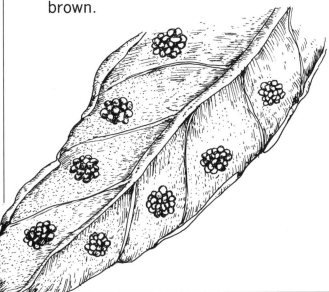

2. Notice how the fruit-dots are arranged on the frond. In some ferns, they are laid out in a definite pattern along the back of the frond (Christmas fern), while in others they are along the edge of the leaflets (maidenhair fern). The walking fern appears to have its fruit-dots scattered randomly over the fronds.
3. If there are no fruit-dots visible on the fronds, the spore cases may be growing on a special part of the frond (interrupted fern or royal fern), or even on separate stalks (cinnamon fern or ostrich fern).

Masses of mosses

If you got down on your hands and knees with a magnifying glass, you could enter the world of mosses. You'd find yourself among mosses that look like palm trees, pine trees, ferns and even feathers. Mosses grow in all these forms and many more—there are more than 20 000 different kinds of mosses. Most mosses grow on land—on soil, trees, rocks or rotting logs—but some moss species can be found underwater in freshwater streams and ponds. Mosses are found everywhere in the world except deserts, so you're bound to come across some in the woods or even in the crack of a city sidewalk. Unlike most plants, green mosses can even thrive beneath a blanket of snow in the winter.

At first glance, you might think all mosses look alike, but that would be like saying all plants look alike. Although mosses share some general characteristics, such as stems, undivided leaves and no roots (they have hair-like parts called rhizoids that function like roots instead), the similarities end there. A close-up look at different kinds of mosses reveals an amazing assortment of size, shape, colour, texture and arrangement of leaves, stems and spore capsules (flower-like pods on thin stalks). Mosses can also change their appearance depending on how wet or dry the growing conditions are.

Get out your magnifying glass and take a look at a sample of dry moss and a sample of wet moss. You'll notice that the leaves of the dried moss are curled up, twisted and grey or brown while the wet moss's leaves are flat and green. Now drop the dry moss into a glass of water. What happens? You should see the stems and leaves straighten out and the green

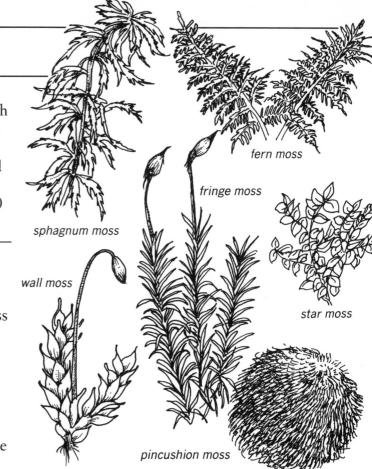

fern moss

fringe moss

sphagnum moss

wall moss

star moss

pincushion moss

colour return. This is what happens to moss in the wild when there is a dry spell followed by rain. Mosses have an amazing ability to "come back to life."

These hardy plants have been important pioneers on near-bare landscapes. Mosses can grow in very shallow soils, creating thicker mats where larger plants can grow. Mosses also provide food for a great variety of animals, and people have found a number of uses for mosses over the years, too. Pioneers mixed moss with clay to fill the cracks in their log cabins. Laplanders even stuffed pillows with moss. Peat, formed from layers of decomposing mosses, is cut and dried for fuel in many countries. Garden nurseries also use peat moss for conditioning soil and keeping plants moist during shipping.

Plant a moss garden

You can start your own moss garden indoors and get to know these fascinating little plants even better.

You'll need:
moss
a knife
a bag
newspaper
a large, wide-mouth glass jar (4 L
    [4 quarts] or more) with lid
peat (available at a garden store)
potting soil
cheesecloth
water
a plant mister
stones or small ornaments (optional)

1. Find some different kinds of mosses growing on rocks, wood or soil. Cut a few shallow squares of moss and bring it home in a bag.

2. Place the moss between sheets of newspaper and leave it to dry for a few days in a warm, dry place.
3. Crumble the old soil away, until just the leafy moss remains. This moss will become the source for your new mosses.
4. Fill your jar half full with an equal mixture of peat and potting soil.
5. Put a layer of cheesecloth over the soil mixture and sprinkle the dried moss on top.

6. Cover with another layer of cheesecloth, and water thoroughly with the plant mister. Always keep the cheesecloth moist.

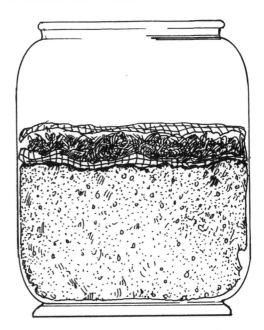

7. Put the lid on the jar and place it in a warm, shady spot. Your moss should start to grow in 6 to 8 weeks.
8. Keep your jar out of direct sunlight. Because it has a lid on, moisture should circulate within the jar and keep the moss damp.
9. Add some interesting stones or small ornaments to your jar to create a miniature landscape.

Aquatic plants

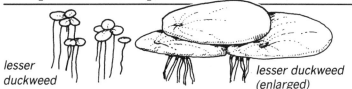

lesser duckweed

lesser duckweed (enlarged)

water meal

water meal (enlarged)

ivy duckweed (enlarged)

Have you ever seen a marsh or small pond covered with a pale green "scum"? If you take a closer look, you'll likely find that what you are looking at is a mass of tiny individual plants called duckweed. Each plant may be only a few millimetres (1/8 inch) across, with even tinier flowers. One species—water meal —is smaller than a pinhead and is the tiniest flowering plant known in the world. Duckweed is a floating plant—its leaves lie on the water's surface and its tiny roots dangle freely below. Other aquatic plants grow completely underwater, while some, like cattails, take the best of both worlds and are rooted in the pond bottom while their leaves are above water.

Unlike land plants, aquatic plants don't have to worry about finding and storing water—it's everywhere. Instead, they have a different challenge—finding and storing air. The water-lily is an example of a plant whose leaves float on the surface while its roots are anchored in the mucky bottom below. Since water loss is not a problem, the leaves don't have a waxy covering or thick cuticle (outermost layer of leaf tissue). And unlike most land plants, the water-lily's leaves have their stomata on their upper surfaces so they can "breathe." The air taken in by the leaves travels to the roots via large channels in the long stems.

What about plants that have no leaves above water? How do they get air? Totally submerged plants, such as milfoils, pondweeds and *Elodea*, can still undergo photosynthesis as much as 6 m (20 feet) below the surface; as long as the water is clear they can get enough sunlight to live. They can also absorb dissolved gases, such as carbon dioxide in the water, directly through their leaves and stems. These plants tend to have many air-storage spaces in their stems and leaves.

Some aquatic plants live a double life—half of the plant grows above water, while the other half grows below water. *Myriophyllum* is a freshwater plant that lives this double life. Its underwater leaves are long and narrow to provide a greater surface area for "breathing." Since the water current continually moves the leaves this way and that, the upper and lower leaf surfaces can both take advantage of the sunlight. The plant parts growing above water look quite different compared to the underwater parts. For instance, the stem has more woody tissue to support it upright in the air. Also, the above-water leaves are smaller and have stomata on their underside only.

You can check out the air pathway in a water-lily by picking a water-lily leaf that has a long stalk. Place the leaf underwater and blow through the stalk. Your air will pass through the tubes in the stem, come out of the stomata in the leaf and make bubbles on the surface.

Grow a garden in water

You can plant an indoor garden without soil by providing your plants with all the nutrients they need in a water solution. The art of soilless gardening is called hydroponics, and it's a growing business around the world. Some of the vegetables you get at the store may have actually been grown in water, not soil.

You'll need:
a knife
a plastic container, such as a margarine or yoghurt tub
a bottle cork
gravel
a plant (try a tomato plant)
hydroponic nutrient solution (available at plant-supply stores)
a bucket

1. Cut a hole in the side of your plastic container, near the bottom, just large enough for your cork. Put the cork in securely.

2. Add 5 cm (2 inches) of gravel to the container. Anchor your plant in the gravel.

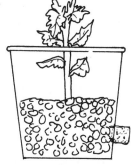

3. Mix up some hydroponic nutrient solution according to the directions on the package and pour it into the container until it is half full. Place the plant in a sunny location.

4. Drain off the water every third day or so by holding your container over the sink or a bucket and removing the cork. Replace the cork and add more nutrient solution. As your plant's roots absorb the nutrient solution over several weeks, you'll see the plant grow, flower and even produce some tasty tomatoes for your family.

Desert plants

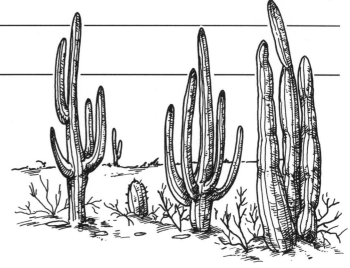

You know what happens to your plants when you forget to water them—they shrivel up and sometimes die. So how do plants survive in the desert where there's hardly any water? Some plants have special desert-proof designs. For instance, imagine a plant that can expand and contract like an accordion, depending on the rainfall. That's what the saguaro cactus does. Its deeply pleated stems expand during brief desert rainfalls so the cactus can absorb as much water as possible. The saguaro is a very large cactus. It can grow to be as tall as a five-storey building and when it's full of water, it can weigh more than an African elephant.

The ability to gather and store water is vital to the survival of many desert plants. The barrel cactus, for example, can last for more than a year without taking a drink. It survives on the water stored in its swollen stems after a heavy rain. Read on to find out how desert plants are adapted to their dry lives.

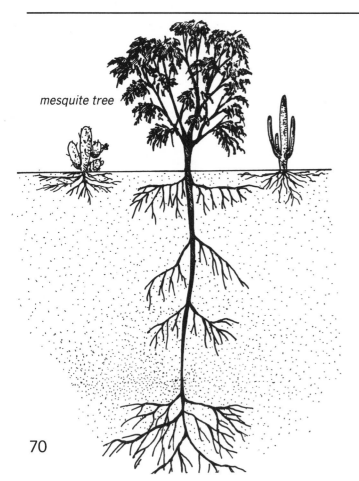

mesquite tree

Roaming roots

If you wanted to dig a well in the desert, you'd look for a mesquite tree first. The mesquite tree sends its long roots down as much as 9 m (30 feet) below the surface to find permanent water reservoirs. You can be sure that a well dug nearby will also find water. In addition to deep tap roots, many desert plants have widely spread, shallow roots that soak up the occasional rains that penetrate just below the surface. Some plants use their underground roots, bulbs or tubers as additional water-storage containers.

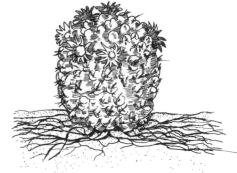

70

Unleafy leaves

Can you guess where the leaves are on this plant? The flat, fleshy, leaf-like parts of some cacti, such as the prickly pear cactus, are actually just swollen stems. The real leaves have been modified into spines to help reduce water loss and keep animals away. Other desert plants have thick leaves with a waxy coating or hairy surfaces to keep the water in. Desert shrubs and trees shed their leaves during periods of drought, just as deciduous trees do in cold winter climates.

Special seeds

Imagine a barren desert landscape. Now picture the same place a few days after a heavy downpour. An almost magical transformation takes place. Suddenly a thousand or more seedlings are sprouting everywhere. Within days they'll grow, flower and set seed for the next generation. Where did the plants come from? The seeds of desert plants are specially adapted to survive for many years and remain dormant in the soil until enough rain falls to allow them to grow and complete their life cycle. So, when the rain comes, the germinating begins and away they grow!

Killer plants

You may take vitamins to supplement your diet and make sure that you're getting all the nutrition you need to stay healthy. Some plants take diet supplements too, but instead of vitamin pills, they eat insects. Insect-eating plants usually grow in nutrient-poor soils. In order to get extra nutrition, especially nitrogen, they capture and digest insects with their specially designed traps. Here's how they do it.

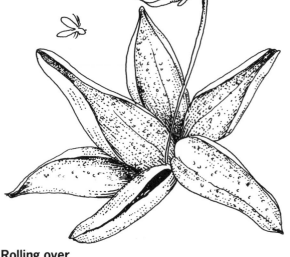

Sliding in

The edges of the pitcher-plant's jug-shaped leaves are coated with a slippery, wax-like material. When an insect lands on a leaf, it takes a slide ride, right into the liquid-filled pitcher below. Long, downward-pointing hairs inside the pitcher stop the insect from crawling out again. Once in the liquid, the insect drowns and is soon digested.

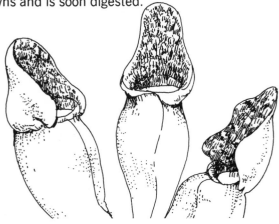

Rolling over

The flat, sticky leaves of the butterwort attract insects. Once the insect is stuck to the leaf, the edges of the leaf roll inward to cover the insect. Inside the trap, the insect is digested.

Mighty mosquitoes

Pitcher-plants capture and digest hundreds of insects in their liquid-filled, jug-shaped leaves. But one kind of mosquito, the Wyeomyia smithii, is too tough even for the pitcher-plant to kill. The mosquito actually uses the plant's pitchers as a home. Its eggs, larvae and pupae thrive in the well-protected pools inside the leaves, and the adults emerge, unharmed by the plant's powers.

Clamming up

The Venus flytrap doesn't really come from the planet Venus — it grows only in North and South Carolina in the United States. It has hinged leaves, fringed with long bristles that are very sensitive to touch. When an insect brushes against the leaf, the leaf snaps shut, like a clam, trapping its dinner inside.

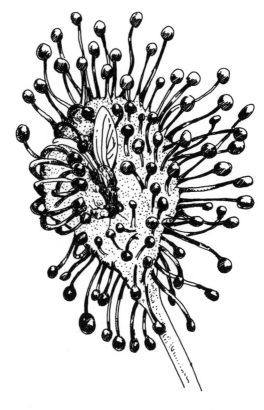

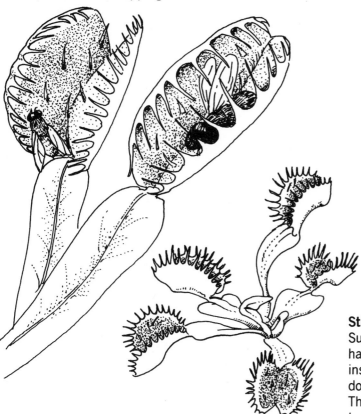

Sticking Down

Sundews look like tiny red suns with long rays of hairs, tipped with dewdrop-like glue. If you were an insect and landed on the sundew, you'd be stuck down on the hairs and wouldn't be able to get free. The hairy leaves would close over you like a temporary stomach and then you'd be absorbed.

Stuck on sundews

Look for the red carpet of sundews growing on rotting logs or on soil among the mosses in boggy areas. Get down on your hands and knees and gently touch one of the hairy leaves with your finger. Slowly pull your finger away. You'll see glue-like strands attached to your finger. These are what trap the insects. Carefully search around the base of the sundew. You should find the leftovers of many meals — the legs, wings

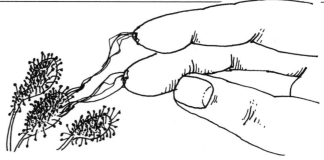

and other body parts of unlucky insects. If you can catch a live insect, such as a mosquito, try feeding the sundew and watch what happens.

Grass gazing

Why is it that you can mow the lawn every week without hurting the grass, but if you did the same to your flower or vegetable garden, even once, you'd probably finish them off for the season? The answer lies in the way your grass grows. Unlike many plants that grow from their tip, grasses have their actively growing cells farther down the stem at the base of the leaf blades and the nodes (see diagram). So, when you cut the ends of the grass blades off with your mower, you're not affecting the growth zone and it quickly replaces the part cut off. That's when you have to get out the lawn mower again!

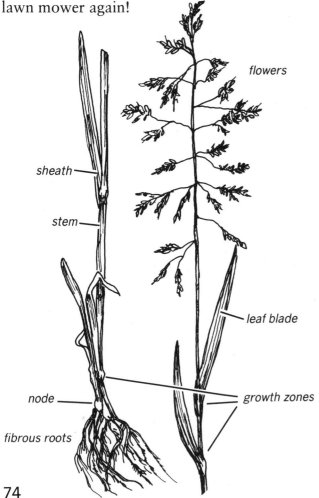

flowers

sheath

stem

leaf blade

node

growth zones

fibrous roots

What good is grass?

Believe it or not, you've probably eaten several varieties of grass already today, especially if you've had any bread, cereal, pasta or rice. All of these foods are made from grass plants. In fact, grasses—mainly corn, wheat, barley, oats, rice, millet and rye—are the most important group of food plants for people in the world. Some form of boiled rice is a basic food for more than half the world's population.

Since we first cultivated grass plants, 10 000 years ago, scientists have continued to improve the basic grass plants for better food production. Even today, wild relatives of these cultivated plants are bred with grass plants to help increase crop resistance to disease, drought and temperature extremes. In addition to feeding people directly, grasses such as sorghum and hay crops make up most of the feed for domesticated animals such as cows and sheep.

Besides providing animals and humans with food, grasses are useful to us in many other ways as well. For instance, bamboo canes are important building materials; reeds are woven into baskets, carpets and furniture (such as wicker); straw is woven into hats; and other grasses are processed to make adhesives, packaging materials and even paper.

Grass up close

You've probably walked on and through millions of blades of grass in your life, but have you ever stopped to take a closer look? Here's your chance. First, head to an unmown ditch or meadow, since the grass will be taller and easier to see and it is more likely to have flowers.

You'll need:
a trowel
a magnifying glass

1. Carefully dig up a small tuft of grass, disturbing the roots as little as possible. Try to find grass that is in flower.

2. Using the illustration on page 74 as a reference, try to find the different parts on your grass, starting with the fibrous roots.

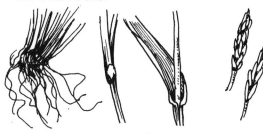

3. Notice how the sheath encloses and protects the stem and then fans out into the leaf blade.

4. Examine the flowers with your magnifying glass. Can you find the pollen-producing anthers and the stigmas? How do you think these flowers are pollinated? Since the flowers are so tiny and not colourful, you can guess that they are not pollinated by insects or birds. When the anthers are ripe with pollen, they hang out from the flower so that the wind can carry the pollen to other plants.

5. When you have finished examining the grass, replant it.

Mushrooms, moulds and fungi

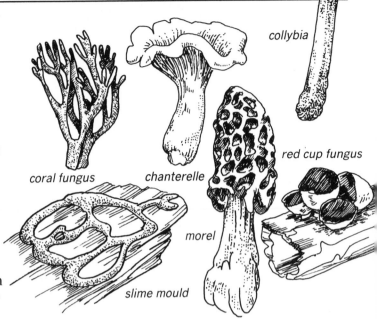

coral fungus

chanterelle

collybia

red cup fungus

morel

slime mould

Eaten any fungi lately? If you've been munching on mushrooms, then your answer will be yes. Mushrooms are a type of fungi. Until recently, fungi were considered plants, but they are now divided into their own kingdom called, you guessed it, the kingdom fungi. (Plants belong to the kingdom plantae.) Other plant-like organisms in the kingdom fungi include moulds and lichens.

The mushroom you eat is only a very small part of the fungus itself. The fungus can be divided into two basic parts: the hyphae (hi-fee) and the fruiting body. Hyphae are root-like threads that spread underground, through rotting wood or other surfaces, sometimes for kilometres (miles), obtaining nourishment for the fungus. The fruiting body is the mushroom part of the fungus that you eat. Most plants produce flowers, which in turn produce seeds, but a fungus grows a fruiting body that produces dust-like spores that are dispersed by the wind. Like the seeds of flowers, the spores are responsible for growing new fungi.

Unlike green plants, fungi have no chlorophyll and can't make their own food through photosynthesis. Fungi feed on dead or living plant tissue, and a few live on animals as parasites. Sometimes the fungus will invade the body of a very small animal, such as a mosquito, and eventually kill the host. Wherever a fungus is growing, its hyphae release chemical substances, called enzymes, into the tissues, where they absorb the nutrients they need to grow. Large animals usually don't suffer too much from a growing fungus. For instance, did you know that athlete's foot, a common skin irritation of people's feet, is caused by a fungus?

Have you ever opened the fridge and seen blue stuff growing on your cheese? That blue, white or greenish powdery substance is also a kind of fungus, called mould. Mould grows on old cheese, bread, fruit or other decaying food. One type of mould, called penicillium, is the source of penicillin, an important disease-fighting drug.

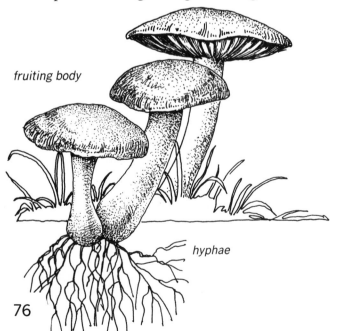

fruiting body

hyphae

Plants and you

From the time you get up in the morning until you go to sleep at night, plants are an important part of your day. Plants make your home and neighbourhood a beautiful place to live, and we couldn't breathe without their help. Ever since people appeared on earth, plants have been an important source of food, shelter, clothing, medicine and tools. Unfortunately, some plants are becoming endangered and extinct because their habitats are being destroyed. Read on to find out what is being done to help save endangered plants and habitats, and discover how you can get involved.

Early uses of plants

Your supper is probably cooked in metal pots, served on a china plate and eaten with a metal knife and fork. But, if you had been born several hundred years ago in North America, before the arrival of the European explorers, chances are you would be eating food cooked in birch-bark pots, and eating it off birch-bark plates, using a birch-bark or wooden spoon. North American natives relied on plants, such as the birch tree, for a wide assortment of materials, as well as food and medicines, that are today manufactured by industries. Try matching up the plants on the next page used by native Indians with their modern-day equivalents. See how many you can get right without peeking at the answers on page 96.

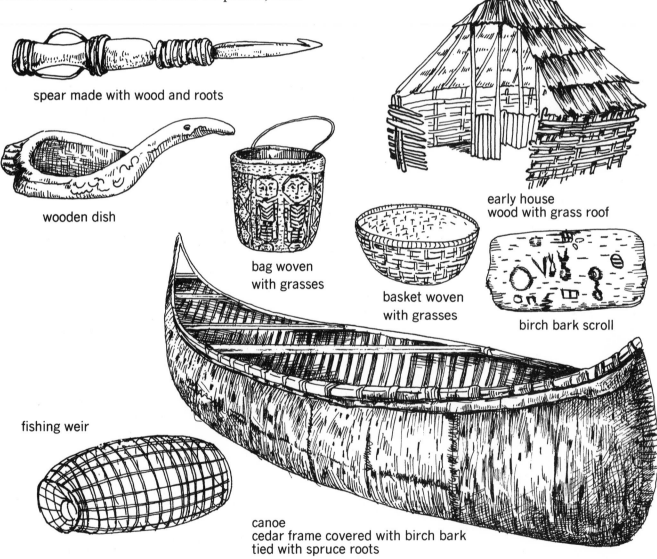

spear made with wood and roots

wooden dish

bag woven with grasses

early house wood with grass roof

basket woven with grasses

birch bark scroll

fishing weir

canoe cedar frame covered with birch bark tied with spruce roots

Match up the plant parts on the left with their modern-day equivalents on the right (answers on page 96).

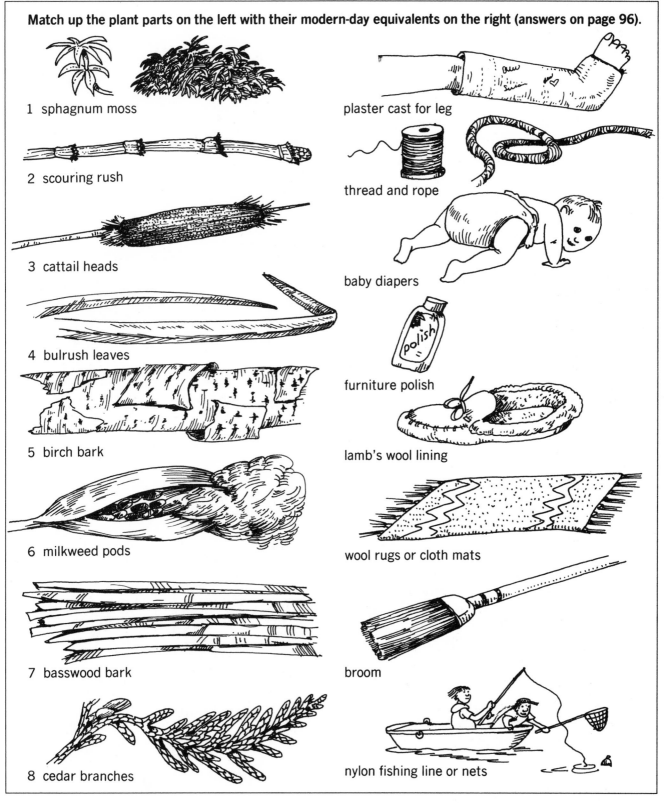

1 sphagnum moss

2 scouring rush

3 cattail heads

4 bulrush leaves

5 birch bark

6 milkweed pods

7 basswood bark

8 cedar branches

plaster cast for leg

thread and rope

baby diapers

furniture polish

lamb's wool lining

wool rugs or cloth mats

broom

nylon fishing line or nets

Wild snacking

When you go hiking, you probably pack a few snacks in case you get hungry. Nature has its own nibbles to offer if you know what to look for. From gum to fruit to salad greens, you can snack in the wild as you go. Always remember, though, never eat anything if you're not positive that it's safe to eat, and never eat plants that have grown in polluted water or along busy roads. Always leave untouched at least ten times more of the plant than you pick. After all, you're not the only wild snacker on the trail—there are lots of animals that feed on wild plants and there have to be enough plants left in order to produce the next generation.

Here are a few snack ideas for your next hike. Read the plant descriptions carefully and take a field guide with you to help you identify the plants mentioned here. Check the list of suggested field guides on page 96.

Chewy trees

You can go to the store if you want some gum, but did you know that you can also go to a spruce tree for a chewy treat? Spring is the best time to look for a freebie from a red or black spruce. Find a spot where the honey-coloured, glossy resin has leaked from a wound in the bark. Pick the hard resin off the tree, scrape it clean and then bite it into little bits. It should soften and turn pink as you chew.

Another chewy tree is the yellow birch. The tender green tips of the branches offer a refreshing wintergreen flavour to freshen your mouth. Just snap off a few centimetres (an inch or two) from the tip of a branch and chew it like you'd chew a stick of licorice.

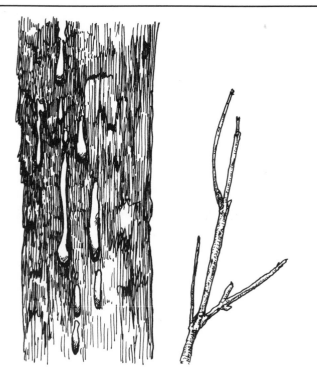

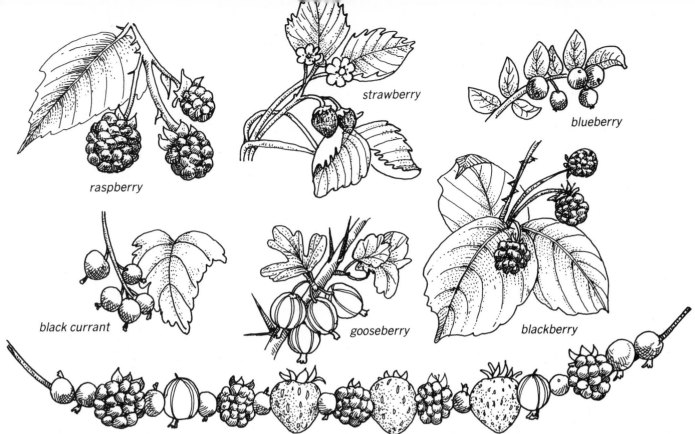

raspberry

strawberry

blueberry

black currant

gooseberry

blackberry

Fruit kabobs

Summer is a great time for finding wild fruits in fields, woods and fence rows, but remember to stay away from the sides of busy roads. Although many wild berries are delicious, you must be careful since different kinds of berries can look alike and some are poisonous. Fruit kabobs can be made with wild or domestic berries—all you need are some long stems of grass. Thread strawberries, blueberries, raspberries or other small, edible fruit onto the stem. Put a hard, unripe berry on first to keep the others from sliding off. Now take a break and enjoy your fruit kabob.

wintergreen

wood-sorrel

Full of flavour

You might recognize the flavour of wintergreen since it is often used to make chewing gum and candy. Now you can chew fresh wintergreen when you find the leaves of this small, shiny green plant in the woods. Simply break off a leaf and chew it to release the fresh, minty flavour.

Wood-sorrel is another small green, leafy plant growing in wood lots. Its lemony, somewhat sour, flavour is very refreshing on its own and also makes a tangy addition to salads or sandwiches.

81

Thirst quencher

So far you've been munching, but what about something to drink? You can make a delicious drink from the fuzzy red fruit of staghorn sumac — a common tree found growing in open fields and at the edges of woods. Collect the berries on your hike and bring them home to make this thirst quencher.

You'll need:
staghorn sumac berries
a large bowl
water
a potato masher
cheesecloth
a colander
a juice jug
a spoon
sugar

1. Put your berries in a large bowl and cover them with cold water.
2. Mash the berries with the potato masher for about 10 minutes to get as much juice out of them as possible.

3. Line your colander with several layers of cheesecloth. Place the colander over your juice jug and pour the mashed fruit and water into the colander. The cheesecloth should keep the berries and most of the tiny hairs that cover them from getting into your juice.

4. Stir sugar into the strained juice a little at a time, adding enough to suit your taste.

Seed snacks

When you scrape out the insides of your Hallowe'en pumpkin, save the seeds and turn them into a tasty snack.

You'll need:
pumpkin seeds
a cookie sheet
vegetable oil
salt
peanuts, sunflower seeds, pine nuts
   (optional)

1. Wash and dry the pumpkin seeds.
2. Spread the seeds on a cookie sheet. Sprinkle them with a little vegetable oil and stir to coat the seeds with oil.

3. Bake at 180°C (350°F) for about 10 minutes, stirring once.
4. Sprinkle with salt to taste.
5. You can mix your toasted pumpkin seeds with peanuts, sunflower seeds or pine nuts for a crunchy, delicious snack.

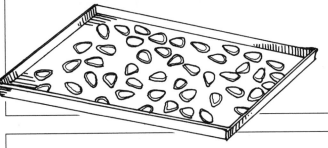

Poisonous plants

Some plants are good to eat, but others can be poisonous and result in symptoms ranging from allergic rashes to death. Just as some plants have thorns or other devices that protect them from being picked, some plants contain chemical toxins (poisons) that protect them from being eaten. Even when one part of a plant is edible, another part of the same plant may be poisonous. For example, rhubarb, whose stems make delicious pies, has poisonous leaves. Poisonous plants may even look like edible ones, such as the resemblance of water hemlock, which is poisonous, to wild parsnip, which is edible. One mistake can be very serious.

Water hemlock (left) and larkspur (right) are poisonous

If you are planning to snack on wild foods, eat only those that you have positively identified with an expert or a good field guide. Experimenting could make you very sick, so stick to the plants you know. Poisonous plants aren't limited to the wild either. Many houseplants, such as philodendron and azalea, and common garden flowers, such as daffodils and larkspur, can be just as dangerous. Your best defence against accidents is to be aware of the dangers and handle all plants with care.

Dyeing with plants

What colours are the clothes you're wearing right now? Chances are you've named several colours, all produced by commercial dyes. But if you had lived before these dyes became available in the 1850s, your clothes would probably have been coloured with natural dyes from plants. You can collect some common plants and try your hand at dyeing. The dandelions suggested here will produce a greenish-yellow colour but you may also want to try some of the other plants listed.

You'll need:
a sharp knife (Ask an adult to help you.)
1 kg (2 lbs) of dandelion leaves and
    stems
2 pots
water
5 mL (1 tsp) alum (available at a
    drugstore)
2 mL (1/2 tsp) washing soda (available at
    a grocery store)
a clean white t-shirt, clean scraps of
    cotton, or whatever material you want
    to dye
a pair of rubber gloves
a strainer

1. Chop the dandelion leaves and stems into small pieces. Place them in a pot, cover with water, and leave them to soak overnight.

2. In another pot, mix the alum and washing soda with 4 L (1 gallon) of water. Soak your cloth in this overnight. The alum and washing soda are called a mordant. This is a substance that helps bind the dye into the material to keep it from running when you wash your t-shirt. Wear rubber gloves when using the mordant because it will dry out your skin. It isn't necessary to use mordants when dyeing with lichens.

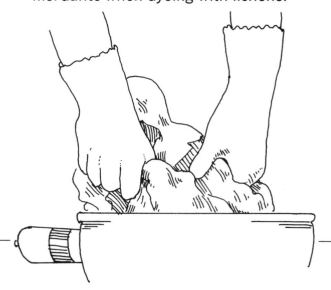

3. The next morning, simmer the plant and water mixture on medium heat for about an hour. If using roots or bark, simmer for 8 to 12 hours. Strain out the plant materials and put them aside. Let the dye water cool.

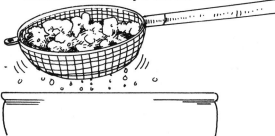

4. Wearing rubber gloves, remove your cloth from the mordant and gently squeeze it out.

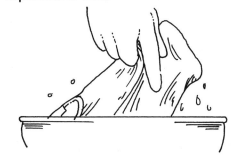

5. Place the cloth in the cooled dye water, add enough water to cover the material, and simmer for 10 to 20 minutes. If dyeing with roots or bark, simmer for 8 hours or more. The longer you simmer the cloth, the deeper the colour will be. The wet cloth will become a slightly lighter colour when dry.

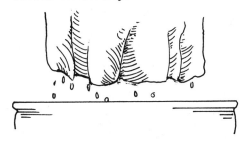

6. Rinse your cloth in hot water and then cool water, until the rinse water is clear. Hang your material to dry inside or in a shady place outside.

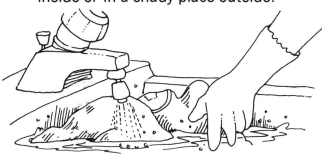

Some common plants for dyeing
Follow the same instructions for dyeing with the plants listed below.

Plant	Colour produced
1. goldenrod flowers	yellow
2. onion skins	dark yellow
3. dandelion roots	red-violet
4. butternut husks	deep tan
5. larkspur petals	blue
6. red hollyhock flowers	pink
7. ragweed leaves	green
8. chamomile flowers	bright yellow
9. dogwood root bark	red
10. cedar root	purple

Plants to the rescue

The medicine man or shaman in North American Indian culture was like the tribal doctor. People came to him for cures for their illnesses. Most of his medicines were made from the plants that grew nearby. Each medicine man knew which plants would cure what ailments and he always had a good supply of a variety of plants to help his people. Today's doctors also rely on wild plants for the medicines they prescribe. Although you don't actually get a jar of dried leaves or powdered roots from the drugstore, almost half of all modern drugs have been derived from wild plants. Some people suffering from leukemia, a cancer of the blood, depend on the drug extracted from a highly endangered plant—the rosy periwinkle—growing in Madagascar. Because of this plant, many leukemia patients are still alive. Millions of other people owe their lives to another plant—the cinchona tree, whose bark was the original source of quinine, a drug used to cure malaria. Research continues daily to find new plants that will save even more lives.

Plants not only cure our diseases, they also keep us healthy by feeding us. More than 85% of the world's food is provided by only 20 or so different kinds of plants. Think about what you ate today. Probably almost everything came from plants either directly—like an apple—or indirectly—like beef that was produced by cattle, who eat plants. The food chains for all wild animals also begin with plants.

Besides being used for medicine and food, plants also perform a number of unseen jobs every day that help to improve our environment. The roots of shoreline plants help bind the soil together to keep water from washing the soil away. Forests and meadows also protect soil from being blown away by wind or carried away by rain water. Many farmers now leave crop stubble on their uncultivated land to protect the soil, instead of ploughing it under and exposing the topsoil to eroding winds and rain.

rosy periwinkle   *cinchona tree flowers*

86

Carbon dioxide and other gases act like panes of glass in a greenhouse by trapping heat and reflecting it back to earth.

Plants also help us to breathe. The tree has been called the oldest, cheapest and most efficient air purifier because of its ability to absorb carbon dioxide and dust particles from the air. By absorbing carbon dioxide, trees are helping to combat the greenhouse effect. Carbon dioxide and other gases that are produced when we burn fuels such as coal and oil act like the panes of glass in a greenhouse by trapping heat and reflecting it back to earth. Scientists are worried that the increase of these greenhouse gases may cause earth to get warmer. This global warming could cause many problems ranging from coastal flooding as polar icecaps melt and cause sea levels to rise, to the loss of our crop-growing areas. In addition to absorbing carbon dioxide, plants also release vast quantities of oxygen and water back into the air during photosynthesis. Since all animals, including humans, depend on oxygen for survival, we could not live without plants.

Your family can put plants to work for you, too. By planting shade trees around your house, you can cut down on your air-conditioning needs. Trees and shrubs planted on the north side or windiest side of your house will keep it warmer in the winter, reducing heating costs.

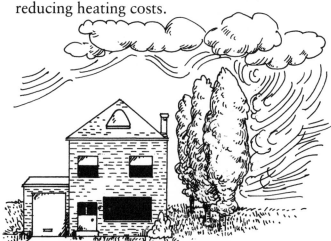

Despite the many valuable roles plants play in the natural world and in human society, species continue to become extinct every day. Because less than 1% of the world's plants have been thoroughly studied, we don't know what we've lost—a cure for diseases, perhaps, or a new food plant to end mass starvation? Without plants, life would be impossible. Turn the page to find out what's happening to our plants, and find out what you can do to help protect what's left.

Plants in danger

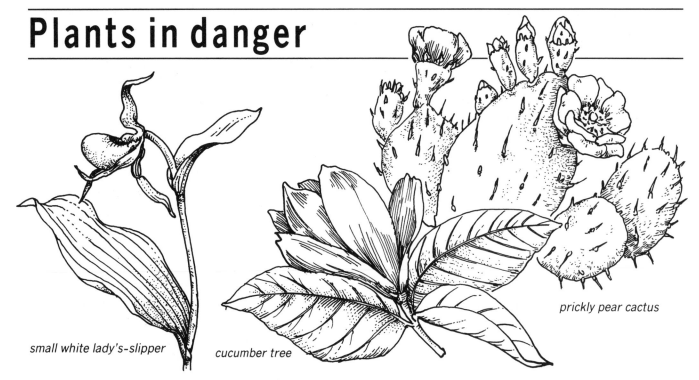

small white lady's-slipper

cucumber tree

prickly pear cactus

If a major highway were going to be built in your neighbourhood, running right across the land where your house is, you would have to move to another place in order to survive. But plants can't just pick themselves up and walk away. Major construction projects, such as highways, simply bulldoze their way through thousands of plants, sometimes destroying rare species and habitats—the places where plants and animals live. In fact, loss of habitat is the major reason most species become endangered and extinct. When a species is endangered, it means that something is causing its population to die out. If the problem isn't solved quickly, the species could become extinct. Extinction means that no more individuals of a species are alive anywhere in the world—they are gone forever.

In Canada, one-third of the nation's rare and endangered plant and animal species grows in the Carolinian forest zone—a unique ecosystem in southwestern Ontario bordering the north shores of Lake Erie and western Lake Ontario. An ecosystem is made up of many living (plants and animals) and non-living (soil, rocks, water) things that share a certain area. The Carolinian zone is home to endangered plants such as the cucumber tree, eastern prickly pear cactus, heart-leaved plantain, small white lady's-slipper, small whorled pogonia and large whorled pogonia orchid. Why are these species endangered? In this relatively small area, much of the original wetland areas have been destroyed by humans. Some of the area has been drained and cleared for agriculture and other parts have been filled in to make more space for housing. And in some parts of the Carolinian zone, very little of the original forests are left because of logging. This loss of natural habitat is the main reason that some species have become endangered, but problems are also caused when people pick or dig up rare plants. Collectors, gardeners or other people who are unaware that the plants need protection are contributing to the endangerment of some plant species.

We need plants

What does it matter if an endangered plant becomes extinct? One of the problems is that no one really knows. We understand so little about the vast majority of the world's 375 000 plant species that losing a plant forever is a bit like throwing away a lottery ticket without checking the numbers first. You may have thrown away a winner.

Each plant species has its own set of genes—a unique set of characteristics that no other plant species has. These characteristics could include the ability to survive in dry or cold climates, or resist diseases. When a plant becomes extinct, we lose the characteristics that might make that plant a future source of food or medicine or enable it to fight off diseases that could wipe out other plants in that species. Scientists call this variety of characteristics genetic diversity, and they're working to save a diverse sample of plants from each species as a source for future research.

You've already read about the vital role plants play in nature's food chains, and the fact that without the oxygen plants provide, nothing could survive on earth. We also depend on plants for food, medicine and many other products, not to mention how much we value them for their beauty. And, for every plant species that becomes extinct, many other organisms that depend on that plant for survival may be doomed along with it.

By setting aside parks and nature reserves as protected areas, we save plants and their habitats.

Endangered spaces

Many endangered plants and animals are threatened with extinction because they are losing their wilderness homes. When our cities grow, or when we start logging an area or using it for agriculture, we wipe out entire wilderness areas. Without help, some of our ecosystems, such as wetlands and rainforests, may be lost forever. You've already read about one way we're working to save some endangered spaces—by setting aside parks or ecological reserves as protected areas—read on to find out about some of our other endangered spaces and what's being done to save them.

Wonderful wetlands

What do ducks, frogs, herons, cattails, muskrat and moose have in common? They all depend on wetlands for survival. Marshes, swamps, fens and bogs—the four basic types of wetlands—not only teem with life, but they also reduce spring flooding and keep local waterways clean. Wetlands help to filter pollutants from runoff water before it enters other water systems.

These valuable wetland areas are disappearing. Most wetlands are drained for farmland, or filled in for the construction of housing, industry and roads, and some wetlands are dredged for harbours and marinas. The results of this destruction can be seen in all areas of wildlife. For instance, over half of all ducks born in North America come from the prairie pothole wetlands, but fewer wetlands mean fewer ducks.

What is being done to save wetlands? Conservation groups, like the Federation of Ontario Naturalists, have lead the way in wetland protection by educating the public about the problem and pushing for government action to help save important wetlands. Local nature clubs have also played a major role in saving wetlands. For example, the Ottawa Field Naturalists saved Alfred Bog, a very important wetland in eastern Ontario. And across North America, Ducks Unlimited has raised millions of dollars to create new wetlands or manage existing ones to improve waterfowl habitat.

Wetlands have also received attention around the world due to an agreement called the Ramsar Convention. This agreement has been signed by many countries and is designed to protect wetlands all over the world.

Home on the range

"O give me a home, where the buffalo roam and the deer and the antelope play . . ." That favourite old tune describes what the prairies of Alberta, Saskatchewan and Manitoba used to look like—sweeping views of native grasslands full of wildlife. It's hard to imagine that there were 60 million buffalo, 30 million pronghorn antelope, deer, elk and much more roaming across the land. But with most of the original grassland habitat ploughed under or built on, a lot of wildlife just can't find a home there anymore. Although the buffalo were killed off by hunters long ago, recent losses of wildlife are mainly due to habitat loss. In fact, one out of every four species on Canada's endangered species list is found on the prairies.

We must save what's left of the original prairie grasslands for the badgers, prairie rattlesnakes, burrowing owls, golden eagles, prairie falcons, feruginous hawks, coyotes, bobcats, pronghorns and countless other plant and animal species that depend on this vital ecosystem. The governments of Saskatchewan and Canada have created Grasslands National Park near Val Marie in Saskatchewan, and World Wildlife Fund, a national conservation group, launched a five year Prairie Conservation Action Plan in 1986 to protect the prairie grasslands that are left.

It's raining, it's pouring . . .

If you thought that rainforests were only found in the tropics, then you're in for a surprise. Canada's west coast supports one of the most spectacular temperate rainforests in North America. In this climate where temperatures are never very hot or very cold, you'll find the nation's oldest forests, largest trees, largest colonies of seabirds and raptors and an incredible array of plants and animals. After a 13 year struggle, a small piece of Canada's rainforest—an area known as South Moresby in the Queen Charlotte Islands—has been saved for future generations.

South Moresby, part of Moresby Island, was declared a national park in 1986 because local residents, environmentalists, politicians and, eventually much of the nation, fought to save it. By talking to everyone from garden clubs, school groups, boardroom executives and media to the Deputy Prime Minister, the word was spread that South Moresby was special and had to be saved. Letters from Canadians and concerned people from other countries poured into the offices of government decision-makers. Even though most of these letters came from people who had never seen South Moresby, they were convinced that it was important to save it for future generations. Every one of those campaigners and letter writers played a role in saving South Moresby.

You can help

You don't need to be a botanist—a person who studies plants—to help save plants from becoming endangered or extinct. Here are some suggestions to get you going.

- Find out what rare plants grow in your area by contacting your local conservation authority or government office for natural resources. Many of these groups have pamphlets on endangered species and protection of natural habitats. If your family or friends own land containing special plants or habitats, make sure they know about it and understand why it's important to protect it.

- If you like to garden, be very careful about what you plant, especially in wilder areas in the country or around a cottage. Some wildflower seed mixtures contain seeds of non-native plants— plants that aren't naturally found in the wild in a certain area. These non-native plant species can take over habitat from plants that are naturally found in an area. This can sometimes lead to the endangerment of native plants. For example, purple loosestrife has become a serious problem in southern Ontario, where it has invaded wetlands and replaced many native plant species almost completely. The loosestrife has very little food or habitat value to native wildlife who are also suffering the loss of native plants.

purple loosestrife

- Enjoy wild plants in their natural setting instead of picking them or digging them up to plant in your own garden. Many wild species, such as orchids, require specific growing conditions and often don't survive when they're transplanted.

- Memberships to conservation groups make unique gifts for friends and family. When you buy a gift membership to The Nature Conservancy of Canada for example, the money is used to save natural areas and endangered wildlife. Some money has recently been used to purchase native prairie habitats for the Grasslands National Park in Saskatchewan. Some groups, such as World Wildlife Fund, even offer special gifts, where a donation will protect an acre of rainforest in Central or South America.

- Find out if there is a local naturalist club in your area and join it to discover more about your natural community. Many small clubs are involved in protecting natural areas and are always looking for help from concerned people like you. For example, the Hamilton Field Naturalists in Ontario purchased a piece of land in the Carolinian forest zone, helping to protect a number of rare species and their habitat. The commitment of time and money, mostly from individual club members, made this possible.

- If you've got some time and imagination, then you can raise money to support conservation groups that are working to save natural habitats and endangered species. Young people all around the world are putting commitment into action by thinking up ways to fund-raise for conservation. Whether it's a bake sale, puppet show, car wash, raffle or door-to-door campaign, you and your friends can do it with some planning and a lot of fun. Why not get your class, hockey team or Guide unit involved, too?

- Put your concerns down on paper. Write a letter to your local member of parliament and ask what work is being done to help endangered plants in your area.

Kid Power

Has anyone ever told you that you're "too young" to do something that you thought was really important? Well, there's a lot you can do to help the environment, and that's *really* important. Just ask Sarah Pugh. Eleven-year-old Sarah was described as one of Canada's most effective conservationists and was one of six winners of a Citation for Environmental Achievement awarded by *Equinox*, a leading Canadian environmental magazine. What did Sarah do? Over three years, this dedicated Chatham, Ontario, student spent her spare time raising $7000 for conservation work stretching from coastal British Columbia to the Gulf of St. Lawrence and the tropical rainforests of Central and South America. From garage sales to soliciting classmates for donations, Sarah counted her pennies and dimes and then put them to work to make the world a better place for all of us. As Sarah says, "No matter what, you can't save the things that are already gone . . . but there are things you can save and can do." What will you do?

Index

Answers

Tree totalling, p. 48

The tree is 41 years old.

Branching out, p. 49

The pine tree is 8 years old.

Early uses of plants, p. 79

1. Sphagnum moss acts like a sponge, absorbing water, and was used to line a baby's pants — probably the first disposable diaper!

2. When rubbed on wood, the natural silica in scouring rush acts as a great polisher.

3. The "fluff" from the cattail seeds was used to line a baby's cradle or a child's slippers to keep them cosy and warm, like lamb's wool.

4. Mats were woven from the long, strong leaves of many water plants including rushes, reeds and cattails.

5. Wet birch bark was moulded around a broken leg or arm and left to dry into a rock-hard, protective splint similar to the plaster casts used by doctors today.

6. The silky threads lining milkweed pods were woven together to make fishing lines and nets for coastal natives.

7. Thread and rope made from basswood bark were widely used for everything from lacing together birch-bark canoes to sewing clothes and stitching wounds.

8. Not only did the dense cedar branches help sweep the floors clean, but they also added a pleasant aroma to the house.

Suggested Field Guides

- *Newcomb's Wildflower Guide*
  by Lawrence Newcomb
  Little, Brown and Company, Boston. 1977.
- *A Field Guide to Wildflowers of Northeastern and North-central North America*
  by Roger Tory Peterson and Margaret McKenny
  Houghton Mifflin Company, Boston. 1968.
- *Native Trees of Canada*
  by R.C. Hosie
  Canadian Forestry Service, Ottawa. 1969.
- *The Audubon Society Field Guide to North American Mushrooms*
  by Gary H. Lincoff
  Alfred A. Knopf, Inc. 1981.
- *A Field Guide to the Ferns*
  by Boughton Cobb
  Houghton Mifflin Company, Boston. 1956.
- *Non-Flowering Plants*. A Golden Nature Guide.
  by F.S. Shuttleworth and H.S. Zim
  Golden Press. 1967.

HIPAA
for Allied Health Careers

Cynthia Newby
CPC

McGraw-Hill
Higher Education

Boston   Burr Ridge, IL   Dubuque, IA   New York   San Francisco   St. Louis
Bangkok   Bogotá   Caracas   Kuala Lumpur   Lisbon   London   Madrid   Mexico City
Milan   Montreal   New Delhi   Santiago   Seoul   Singapore   Sydney   Taipei   Toronto

HIPAA FOR ALLIED HEALTH CAREERS

Published by McGraw-Hill, a business unit of The McGraw-Hill Companies, Inc., 1221 Avenue of the Americas, New York, NY, 10020. Copyright © 2009 by The McGraw-Hill Companies, Inc. All rights reserved. No part of this publication may be reproduced or distributed in any form or by any means, or stored in a database or retrieval system, without the prior written consent of The McGraw-Hill Companies, Inc., including, but not limited to, in any network or other electronic storage or transmission, or broadcast for distance learning.

Some ancillaries, including electronic and print components, may not be available to customers outside the United States.

This book is printed on acid-free paper.

5 6 7 8 9 0 CTP/CTP 12 11

ISBN   978-0-07-337412-3
MHID   0-07-337412-1

Vice President/Editor in Chief: *Elizabeth Haefele*
Vice President/Director of Marketing: *John E. Biernat*
Senior sponsoring editor: *Debbie Fitzgerald*
Managing developmental editor: *Patricia Hesse*
Executive marketing manager: *Roxan Kinsey*
Lead media producer: *Damian Moshak*
Director, Editing/Design/Production: *Jess Ann Kosic*
Project manager: *Marlena Pechan*
Senior production supervisor: *Janean A. Utley*

Designer: *Marianna Kinigakis*
Interior designer: *Kay Lieberherr*
Media project manager: *Mark A. S. Dierker*
Outside development house: *Wendy Langerud, S4Carlisle Pubishing Services*
Typeface: *10.5/13 New Aster*
Compositor: *Aptara, Inc.*
Printer: *CTPS*

Library of Congress Cataloging-in-Publication Data

Newby, Cynthia.
    HIPAA for allied health careers / Cynthia Newby.
        p. ; cm.
    Includes index.
    ISBN-13: 978-0-07-337412-3 (alk. paper)
    ISBN-10: 0-07-337412-1 (alk. paper)
    1. Medical records—Law and legislation—United States. 2. United States.
Health Insurance Portability and Accountability Act of 1996. 3. Allied health
personnel—United States—Handbooks, manuals, etc. I. Title.
    [DNLM: 1. United States. Health Insurance Portability and Accountability
Act of 1996. 2. Insurance, Health—legislation & jurisprudence—United States.
3. Allied Health Personnel—United States. 4. Confidentiality—legislation
& jurisprudence—United States. 5. Medical Records—legislation & jurisprudence—
United States. W 32.5 AA1 N535h 2009]
    KF3827.R4N52 2009
    344.7304′1—dc22

                                                                    2007051770

The Internet addresses listed in the text were accurate at the time of publication. The inclusion of a Web site does not indicate an endorsement by the authors or McGraw-Hill, and McGraw-Hill does not guarantee the accuracy of the information presented at these sites.

www.mhhe.com

Brief Contents

Contents

Preface

Of the many federal initiatives in the area of health care, HIPAA has arguably had the widest effect on those working in allied health. HIPAA aims to enforce national standards for the health care information that is communicated while also protecting information privacy. Its concepts affect health care claims, electronic health records, and all other forms of communication in the delivery of health care.

HIPAA for Allied Health Careers is specifically designed to teach the concepts and knowledge allied health workers must understand to correctly handle patients' protected health information (PHI) and to comply with all HIPAA regulations, including:

❯ Administrative Simplification
❯ Privacy Rule
❯ Security Rule
❯ Transactions, Code Sets, and National Identifier Standards
❯ Final Enforcement Rule and Compliance to Avoid Fraud and Abuse

TO THE STUDENT

The structure and features of *HIPAA for Allied Health Careers* will help you learn the key concepts and regulations of HIPAA. The text/workbook is organized into five chapters. Each provides foundational knowledge and practical information:

❯ Chapter 1, *The Goal of HIPAA: Administrative Simplification,* overviews the reasons for the federal legislation and why the rules are critically important.

❯ Chapter 2, *The HIPAA Privacy Standards,* explains how to protect the privacy of health information while providing health care to patients

❯ Chapter 3, *The HIPAA Security Standards,* describes the safeguards that are in place to protect health information as it is communicated

❯ Chapter 4, *The HIPAA Transactions, Code Sets, and National Identifier Standards,* discusses the nationally mandated diagnosis and procedure codes as well as the formats that must be used to transmit health care claims

❯ Chapter 5, *HIPAA Enforcement,* explains how government agencies enforce HIPAA and describes the steps health care providers can take to comply with HIPAA regulations

Key features are:

❯ Compliance Tips—*highlight key points for actions that follow important regulations*
❯ FYI boxes—*focus on interesting and involving information*
❯ Internet-based activities—*reinforce the essential skills of researching and evaluating Internet sources*
❯ What Is Your Opinion? Case Studies—*require critical thinking about the chapter's material*
❯ Internet Resources—*provide online references for staying up to date in the future*
❯ HIPAA Cautions—*focus on ways to avoid actions that do not comply with HIPAA*
❯ Decision Trees and Forms—*support communication skills*

What Every Instructor Needs to Know

WELCOME TO HIPAA FOR ALLIED HEALTH CAREERS!

As you know, the field of health care is in the midst of an enormous transition from paper-based to electronic transactions, requiring protection of patients' private health information. While the demand for graduates with a background in allied health exceeds the supply, students entering the field today also need a basic understanding of how to protect health information in their work settings. That is the purpose of this text, which was developed specifically for students in allied health programs.

TEACHING SUPPLEMENTS

For the Instructor

Instructor's Manual, posted to the Online Learning Center, www.mhhe.com/NewbyHIPAA includes:

> Course overview
> Chapter-by-chapter lesson plans
> Solutions
> Correlation tables: SCANS, AAMA Role Delineation Study Areas of Competence (2003), and AMT Registered Medical Assistant Certification Exam Topics.

Online Learning Center (OLC), www.mhhe.com/NewbyHIPAA, Instructor Resources include:

> Instructor's Manual in Word and PDF format
> Instructor's PowerPoint® presentation of Chapters 1 through 5.
> Electronic testing program featuring McGraw-Hill's EZ Test. This flexible and easy-to-use program allows instructors to create tests from book specific items. It accommodates a wide range of question types and instructors may add their own questions. Multiple versions of the test can be created and any test can be exported for use with course management systems such as WebCT, Blackboard, or PageOut.
> Links to professional associations
> PageOut link
> Updates

For the Student

Online Learning Center (OLC), www.mhhe.com/NewbyHIPAA includes additional chapter quizzes and other review activities.

Acknowledgments

HIPAA Advisory Board

Donna Kyle-Brown
Donna Gauwitz
Charlene Harrison
Karen Judson
Nina Therier

Reviewers

Terri Hock
Apollo College
Albuquerque, NM

Carol Lee Jarrell MLY, AHI
Department Chair-Medical
Brown Mackie College-
Merrillville
Merrillville, IN

Christine Malone MHA
Everett Community College
Everett, WA

Kathy Plankenhorn RNC, NP,
MSN
Ivy Tech Community College
Richmond, IN

Cindy Thompson RN, RMA,
MA, BS
Davenport University
Bay City, MI

Barbara Tietsort
University of Cincinnati
Cincinnati, OH

Marilyn M. Turner RN, CMA
Ogeechee Technical College
Statesboro, GA

The Goal of HIPAA: Administrative Simplification

1

LEARNING OUTCOMES

After studying this chapter, you should be able to:

1. Discuss the reasons for passage of the Health Insurance Portability and Accountability Act (HIPAA).
2. Differentiate between the two major provisions of HIPAA, Title I and Title II.
3. Discuss the improvements to health insurance coverage under Title I.
4. Identify the five key provisions of HIPAA Administrative Simplification.
5. Define the concept of preemption.
6. List the four areas in which standards under HIPAA Administrative Simplification have been legislated.
7. Describe the HIPAA rule-making process.
8. Describe the types of facilities and health care professionals who are considered covered entities under HIPAA.
9. Differentiate between a covered entity and a business associate.
10. Describe how allied health personnel can keep up with HIPAA standards and enforcement in their careers.

KEY TERMS

Administrative Simplification
business associate (BA)
Centers for Medicare and Medicaid Services (CMS)

clearinghouse
Consolidated Omnibus Budget Reconciliation
    Act (COBRA)

covered entity (CE)

creditable coverage

Department of Health and Human
    Services (HHS)

direct provider

electronic data interchange (EDI)

Federal Employees Health Benefits
    (FEHB) program

Federal Register

group health plan (GHP)

Health Insurance Portability and Accountability
    Act (HIPAA) of 1996

health insurance reform

health plan

indirect provider

Notice of Proposed Rule-Making
    (NPRM)

Office for Civil Rights (OCR)

preemption

provider

small health plan

Title I (health insurance reform)

Title II (Administrative Simplification)

transaction

Why This Chapter Is Important

The acronym HIPAA stands for the Health Insurance Portability and Accountability Act of 1996. Initiated by Senators Edward Kennedy and Nancy L. Kassebaum, HIPAA began as a response to public concern over people who were denied health insurance when they changed jobs. The final version enacted by Congress, however, was much broader in scope, and its impact continues more than a decade after passage. In addition to protecting the portability of health insurance, the law sets standards for the use of electronic technology by health care organizations. It establishes standards for protecting peoples' medical information during its electronic exchange. HIPAA also imposes fines and possible prison terms for those who violate its provisions.

HIPAA affects everyone who works in allied health careers, so knowing how to comply with its standards is essential. Allied health personnel must know how to protect patients' personal health information, how to respond to requests for this information from other parties, and how to safeguard the electronic exchange of information on behalf of patients.

HIPAA (the **Health Insurance Portability and Accountability Act of 1996**) became Public Law 104-191 on August 21, 1996. The purposes of the act are to:

> Improve the efficiency and effectiveness of health care delivery by creating a national framework for health privacy protection that builds on efforts by states, health systems, and individual organizations and individuals

> Protect and enhance the rights of patients by providing them with access to their health information and controlling the inappropriate use or disclosure of that information

> Improve the quality of health care by restoring trust in the health care system among consumers, health care professionals, and the multitude of organizations and individuals committed to the delivery of care

HIPAA has two parts. Title I, health insurance reform, is the law on continuation of health insurance coverage when individuals change jobs. Title II, known as the Administrative Simplification standards, affects individuals' private health information and is the major subject of this program. As you study this introductory chapter, consider the importance of HIPAA, thinking about which aspects are most important in your community and for your chosen allied health career.

"No, it's not a female Hippopotamus. Anyone else know?"

Source: Cartoon by Dave Harbaugh from HCPro Health Care Humor. Reprinted by permission of HCPro.

Title I: Health Insurance Reform

Many people in the United States have medical insurance coverage through government entitlement programs such as Medicare and Medicaid. These individuals have federal rights concerning their insurance. For example, no medical condition can be used to block a person from Medicare eligibility.

Other people are covered by private insurance that is offered by their employers. Their rights regarding eligibility for coverage were limited before passage of HIPAA **Title I, health insurance reform.**

INSURANCE BACKGROUND

The three major sources of private health insurance are:

1. Employer-sponsored group health plans

2. The Federal Employees Health Benefits program

3. Individual plans

Many employees have medical insurance coverage under **group health plans (GHP)** that their employers offer. Some employers buy this coverage from insurance companies; others cover the costs of employee medical benefits by creating self-funded (or self-insured) health plans that do not pay premiums to an insurance carrier or a managed care organization. Instead, self-funded health plans "insure themselves" and assume the risk of paying directly for medical services, setting aside funds with which to pay.

The more than 8 million federal employees, retirees, and their families are offered medical insurance coverage through the **Federal Employees Health Benefits (FEHB) program.** FEHB is administered by the federal government's Office of Personnel Management (OPM).

When employment does not offer coverage, individual health plans (IHP) can be purchased. Almost 10 percent of people with private health insurance have individual plans. People often elect to enroll in individual plans, although coverage is expensive, in order to continue their health insurance between jobs. Purchasers also include self-employed entrepreneurs, students, recent college graduates, and early retirees.

INTERNET RESOURCE

State Departments of Insurance

www.naic.org/
state_web_map.htm

PORTABILITY AND REQUIRED COVERAGE: COBRA AND HIPAA

Some types of insurance are regulated by state law, and state departments of insurance establish coverage requirements and accept appeals from people who may have been unfairly treated by insurance carriers. However, employer-sponsored group health plans are regulated by the Employee Retirement Income and Security Act of 1974 (ERISA), not by state law. Federal laws have been required to hold these plans accountable for equitable treatment of all individuals. A number of regulations govern group health coverage in situations such as changing jobs, pregnancy, and certain illnesses. The Federal Employees Health Benefit program has similar temporary continuation of coverage provisions under the Federal Employees Health Benefits Amendments Act of 1988.

COBRA

The **Consolidated Omnibus Budget Reconciliation Act (COBRA)** (1985; amended 1986) gives an employee who is leaving a job the right to continue health coverage under the employer's plan for a limited time at his or her own expense. COBRA participants usually pay more than do active employees, since the employer usually pays part of the premium for an active employee, while a COBRA participant generally pays the entire premium. However, COBRA is ordinarily less expensive than individual health coverage. The COBRA home page is shown in Figure 1-1.

HIPAA

Title I of HIPAA (1996) made three changes to COBRA continuation coverage, which took effect in 1997. First, HIPAA includes protections for coverage under group health plans by limiting exclusions for

INTERNET RESOURCE

COBRA Information

www.dol.gov/ebsa

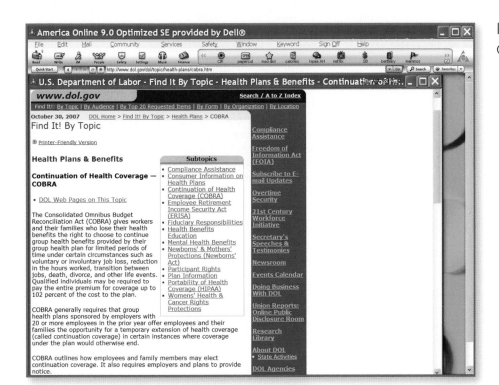

Figure 1-1
COBRA Home Page.

preexisting conditions and prohibits discrimination against employees based on their health status. For cost control, many private plans limit or exclude coverage of patients' previous illnesses or conditions. HIPAA regulates these exclusions. Plans can "look back" into the patient's medical history for a period of six months to find conditions that they will exclude, but they cannot look back for a longer period. Also, the preexisting condition limitation cannot last more than twelve months after the effective date of coverage (eighteen months for late enrollees).

Second, HIPAA also gives some individuals a special opportunity to enroll in a new plan in certain circumstances. The patient's previous **creditable coverage** must be taken into account when an employee joins a new plan. Creditable coverage is health insurance under a group health plan, health insurance, or the Medicaid program known as SCHIP. The previous plan is required to give the employee a certificate of coverage when coverage ends. The employee gives this document to the new plan because having previous coverage can reduce the length of limitation the new plan can put in the person's new insurance policy.

Third, in some situations, HIPAA gives individuals the right to purchase individual coverage if no group health plan coverage is available to them and they have exhausted COBRA or other continuation coverage.

ADDITIONAL LAWS AFFECTING THE AVAILABILITY OF INSURANCE COVERAGE

Three other federal laws also govern private insurance coverage:

1. The Newborns' and Mothers' Health Protection Act provides protections for mothers and their newborn children relating to the length of hospital stays after childbirth. Unless state law says otherwise,

> **COMPLIANCE TIP**
>
> **State Law and Preexisting Condition Exclusions**
>
> The six-month look-back period and the length of the preexisting condition limitation extension period are shortened under the laws of some states.

> **COMPLIANCE TIP**
>
> **Pregnancy and Childbirth Rules**
>
> A preexisting condition exclusion cannot be applied to pregnancy, to a newborn adopted child, or to a child placed for adoption if the child is covered under a group health plan within thirty days after birth, adoption, or placement for adoption.

plans cannot restrict benefits for a hospital stay for childbirth to less than forty-eight hours following a vaginal delivery or ninety-six hours following delivery by cesarean section. Plans are permitted to require preauthorization for the hospitalization.

2. The Women's Health and Cancer Rights Act provides protections for individuals who elect breast reconstruction after a mastectomy. Plans must cover all stages of breast reconstruction, procedures on the other breast to produce a symmetrical appearance, prostheses, and treatment of physical complications of the mastectomy, including lymphodema. State laws may be more restrictive than this act and may require a minimum length of hospitalization after the procedure.

3. The Mental Health Parity Act provides for parity (equality) with medical and surgical benefits when plans set lifetime or annual dollar limits on mental health benefits (except for substance abuse or chemical dependency).

Title II: Administrative Simplification

Title II of HIPAA, known as **Administrative Simplification,** substantially affected the entire health care industry. Implementation of its rules changed administrative, financial, and case management policies and procedures. The law contained strict new requirements for the uniform transfer of electronic health care data such as for billing and payment; new patient rights regarding personal health information, including the right to access this information and to limit its disclosure; and broad new security rules that health care organizations must put in place to safeguard the confidentiality of patients' medical information.

PURPOSE AND EXTENT OF ADMINISTRATIVE SIMPLIFICATION

The U.S. Congress passed an act with provisions for administrative simplification because of concern over the rising costs of health care. A significant portion of every health care dollar spent in the United

States goes to the overhead associated with administrative and financial transactions, such as filing claims for payment, checking patient eligibility for benefits, requesting authorization for services, and notifying providers of payments. Estimates of current administrative costs in the health care industry range from 15 percent to 30 percent, much higher than in any other industry.

Many of these transaction-related costs are associated with the massive number of paper forms used and with the significant variation in formatting the portion of these transactions that are processed via the Internet. It is generally agreed that the health care industry could achieve much greater efficiency if common business transactions were standardized and handled digitally. Many industry experts think the cost savings from e-commerce could be in the range of billions of dollars for both providers and payers.

The Administrative Simplification provisions encourage the use of **electronic data interchange (EDI).** EDI is the computer-to-computer exchange of routine business information using publicly available standards. People working in allied health careers use EDI to exchange health information about patients among physicians and insurance companies. Each electronic exchange is a **transaction,** which is the electronic equivalent of a business document.

EDI transactions are not visible in the way that an exchange of paperwork, such as a letter, is. An example of a nonmedical transaction is the process of getting cash from an ATM. In an ATM transaction, the computer-to-computer exchange is made up of computer language that is sent and answered between the machines. This exchange happens behind the scenes. It is documented on the customer's end with the transaction receipt that is printed; the bank also has a record at its location.

ADMINISTRATIVE SIMPLIFICATION STANDARDS

The Administrative Simplification provisions of HIPAA (Title II) required the **Department of Health and Human Services (HHS)** to establish national standards for electronic health care transactions and national identifiers for providers, health plans, and employers. It also addressed the security and privacy of the health data that are exchanged electronically. These were the five basic provisions:

1. *Standards for electronic health information transactions:* Within eighteen months of enactment of HIPAA, HHS had to adopt standards from among those already approved by private standards-developing organizations for certain electronic health care transactions, including claims, enrollment, eligibility, payment, and coordination of benefits. These standards also had to address the security of electronic health information systems.

2. *Mandate on providers and health plans, and timetable:* Providers and health plans had to start using the standards for the specified electronic transactions twenty-four months after they were adopted.

3. *Privacy:* HHS had to recommend privacy standards for health information to Congress twelve months after enactment of HIPAA. If Congress did not enact privacy legislation within three years of enactment, HHS had the authority to set privacy regulations for individually identifiable electronic health information.

4. *Preemption of state law:* Under the concept of **preemption,** HIPAA rules supersede state laws, except where HHS decides that a state law is necessary to prevent fraud and abuse, to ensure appropriate state regulation of insurance or health plans, to address controlled substances, or for other purposes. However, HIPAA privacy regulations do not preempt state laws that impose more stringent requirements. For example, group health plans must follow federal and state laws that mandate coverage of specific benefits or treatments and access to care. When a state law is more restrictive than the related federal law, the state law is followed.

5. *Penalties:* The bill imposes civil money penalties and prison for certain violations.

Since this umbrella act was passed, a number of HIPAA standards have been made into law. The three main areas that are governed by these laws are privacy, security, and electronic transactions. A fourth area of importance is enforcement of HIPAA rules.

HIPAA Privacy Standards

The privacy standards cover patients' health information. The goal of the Privacy Rule is to protect personal health information. The privacy requirements are the topic of Chapter 2 of this program.

HIPAA Security Standards

The security standards present the administrative, technical, and physical safeguards that are required to protect patients' health information. The Security Rule is the topic of Chapter 3 of this program.

HIPAA Electronic Transactions

The electronic transactions standards require entities that do business electronically to all use the same health care transactions, code sets, and identifiers. The goal of the transactions and code sets rule is to improve the efficiency of the business of health care. HIPAA-covered transactions include such activities as health care claims sent by physicians and hospitals to insurance companies, payments by the insurance companies, and employee enrollment information sent by employers to their insurance companies. Electronic transactions are the topic of Chapter 4 of this program.

HIPAA Enforcement

Investigating complaints that HIPAA regulations have been violated is the job of two government agencies. The privacy standards are enforced by the Office for Civil Rights (OCR). The security and electronic transactions standards are enforced by the Centers for Medicare and

Medicaid Services (CMS). The HIPAA enforcement rule is the topic of Chapter 5 of this program.

The **Office for Civil Rights (OCR)** is an agency of HHS. It is charged with enforcing the privacy standards, because the right to privacy is considered a civil right.

The main federal government agency responsible for health care is the **Centers for Medicare and Medicaid Services,** known as **CMS** (formerly the Health Care Financing Administration, or HCFA). Also an agency of HHS, CMS administers the Medicare and Medicaid programs to more than 90 million Americans. CMS implements annual federal budget acts and laws such as the Medicare Prescription Drug, Improvement, and Modernization Act that helps Medicare beneficiaries pay for drugs and for annual physical examinations.

CMS also performs activities to ensure the quality of health care, such as:

> Regulating all laboratory testing other than research performed on humans

> Preventing discrimination based on health status for people buying health insurance

> Researching the effectiveness of various methods of health care management, treatment, and financing

> Evaluating the quality of health care facilities and services

CMS policy is often the model for the health care industry. When a change is made in Medicare rules, for example, private payers often adopt a similar rule. When federal laws regarding Americans' rights to health care are enacted, CMS often has a key role in developing and implementing them.

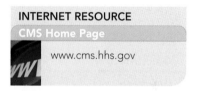

INTERNET RESOURCE
CMS Home Page
www.cms.hhs.gov

RULE-MAKING PROCESS

Since the passage of the base HIPAA legislation, the Department of Health and Human Services has released a stream of HIPAA Administrative Simplification rules. HHS has also issued interpretive guidance documents and extensions of compliance deadlines. The process is as follows:

1. A proposed rule is drafted and then approved within the government. Three agencies—the HHS Data Council Committee on Health Data Standards, advisers to the HHS, and the Office of Management and Budget (OMB)—review the proposal.

2. The proposed rule, a document called the **Notice of Proposed Rule-Making (NPRM),** is released for public comment. The NPRM is published in the *Federal Register* and on the Administrative Simplification home page (see Figure 1-2).

3. The public is given a period of time to provide comments. When there is considerable public controversy over a proposal, the comment period can extend for as long as eighteen months.

INTERNET RESOURCE
Federal Register Home Page
www.gpoaccess.gov/fr/
index.html

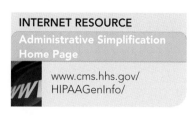

INTERNET RESOURCE
Administrative Simplification
Home Page
www.cms.hhs.gov/
HIPAAGenInfo/

Figure 1-2

HIPAA Administrative Simplification Home Page

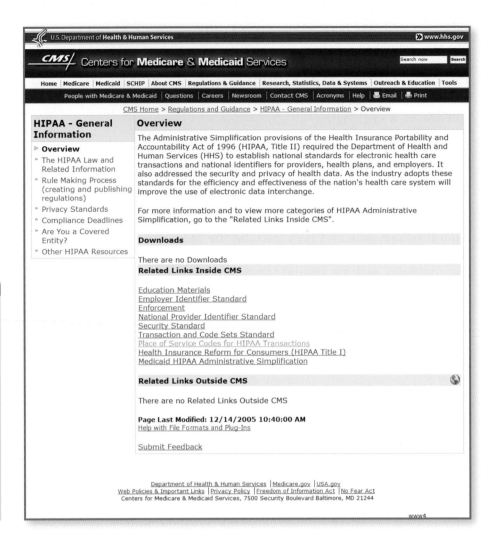

4. HHS revises the rule and publishes the comments and reactions.

5. The final rule is published in the *Federal Register* and on the Administrative Simplification home page with the date on which compliance is required (see Figure 1-3). The standards become effective twenty-four months after adoption for most organizations and thirty-six months after adoption for small health plans.

1-2   Thinking It Through

According to the concept of preemption, which rule, the state's or HIPAA's, governs in the following cases?

1. State law requires health plans to cover an annual breast cancer screening mammogram for women and an annual prostate cancer screening for men; HIPAA does not.

2. HIPAA law requires the medical records of patients who are minors to be securely stored for ten years; the applicable state law requires several years.

3. State law requires an authorization from a patient for a physician to release appropriate parts of a patient's medical record to the patient's insurance company for claim payment; HIPAA permits this release without specific authorization from the patient.

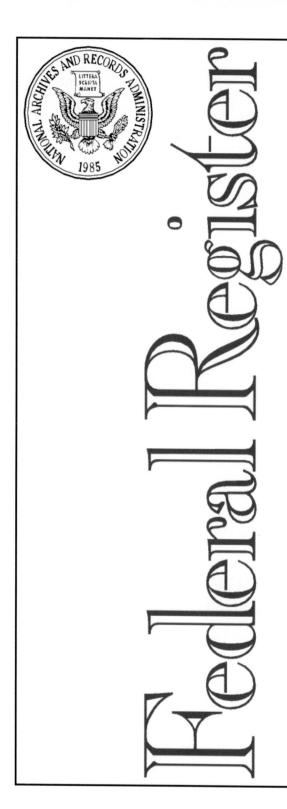

Thursday,
February 16, 2006

Part III

Department of Health and Human Services

Office of the Secretary

45 CFR Parts 160 and 164
HIPAA Administrative Simplification:
Enforcement; Final Rule

Covered Entities: Complying with HIPAA

Figure 1-3
Title Page from *Federal Register:* HIPAA Final Enforcement Rule

Health care organizations that are required by law to obey the HIPAA regulations are called **covered entities (CEs).** A covered entity is an organization or a health care professional who (1) provides health care in the normal course of business and (2) electronically sends any

Figure 1-4
Covered Entity Decision Tree

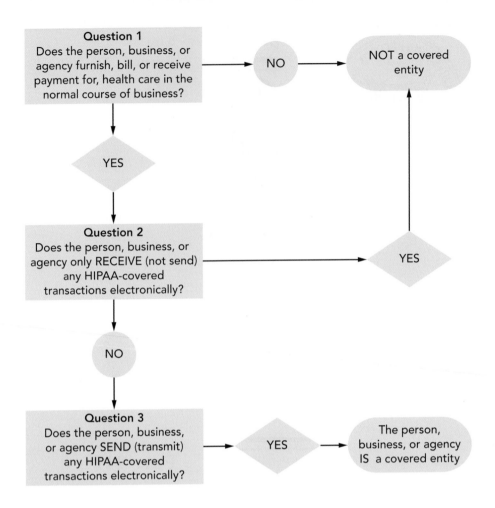

information that is protected under HIPAA. Figure 1-4 presents a decision tree for identifying a covered entity.

COVERED ENTITIES: HEALTH PLANS, PROVIDERS, AND CLEARINGHOUSES

Under HIPAA, three types of CEs must follow the regulations:

1. Health plans

2. Providers

3. Clearinghouses

Health Plans

Under HIPAA, a **health plan** is an insurance plan that provides or pays for medical care. Health plans include:

〉 Group health plans, including insured and self-insured plans (including those with fifty or more participants or administered by an entity other than the employer)

〉 Health insurance issuers, including HMOs (all state-regulated insurance companies)

〉 Medicare Part A, Part B, and the Medicare Advantage program under Parts C and D

HIPAA for Allied Health Careers

> Medicaid

> Issuers of Medicare supplemental policies

> Issuers of long-term care policies, excluding a nursing home fixed-indemnity policies

> Employee welfare benefit plans or other arrangements that are established or maintained for the purpose of offering or providing health benefits to the employees of two or more employers

> TRICARE, the health care program for active military personnel

> CHAMPVA, the veterans health care program

> The Indian Health Service program

> The Federal Employees Health Benefits program

> Approved state child health plans under Title XXI of the Social Security Act

> High-risk pools established under state law to provide health insurance coverage or comparable coverage to eligible individuals

> Other individual or group plans, or combinations of individual or group plans, that provide or pay for the cost of medical care under the Public Health Service Act

The following types of benefits are exempt from the HIPAA standards, even when provided by a health plan:

> Accident or disability income insurance

> General and automotive liability insurance

> Workers' compensation

> Automobile medical payment insurance

> Coverage for on-site medical clinics

FYI

Small Health Plans

A **small health plan** is a health plan with annual receipts of $5 million or less.

HIPAA ⚠ CAUTION

Property and Casualty Insurance Programs

Under HIPAA, property and casualty insurance programs are not covered entities.

Providers

Health care **providers** are people or organizations that furnish, bill, or are paid for health care in the normal course of business. They include:

> Hospitals

> Critical access hospitals

> Skilled nursing facilities

> Comprehensive outpatient rehabilitation facilities

> Hospices

> Home health agencies

> Pharmacies

> Physician practices

> Dental practices

Most providers are CEs under HIPAA. The only exceptions are those that do not send any claims (or other HIPAA transactions) electronically *and* do not employ any other firm to send electronic claims for them. Since CMS requires providers to send Medicare claims electronically unless they employ fewer than ten full-time or equivalent employees, many providers have moved to EDI for the health claim process.

FYI

"Covered Entities" May Expand in the Future

The National Committee on Vital and Health Statistics has advised HHS to expand the definition of HIPAA covered entities because . . . many new entities . . . fall outside HIPAA's statutory definition of "covered entity." For example, health information exchanges, regional health information organizations, record locator services, community access services, fitness clubs, home testing laboratories, massage therapists, nutritional counselors, "alternative" medicine practitioners, urgent care facilities, and medical records banks do not currently fall under HIPAA regulations.

COMPLIANCE TIP

BA Exceptions

Work done at the request of an employer, such as preemployment drug testing or a physical exam, does not require the provider to establish a BA agreement with the employer.

> Chiropractors
> Podiatrists
> Osteopaths
> Therapists
> Laboratories

Providers that have a direct treatment relationship with patients, such as physician practices, therapists, and chiropractors, are called **direct providers.** In contrast, an **indirect provider** has an indirect treatment relationship with a patient. An example is a laboratory that reports test results to the provider who then treats the patient.

Clearinghouses

Health care **clearinghouses** are companies that help providers handle such electronic transactions as submitting claims and that manage electronic medical record systems. Clearinghouses process health information by converting it into a format that meets HIPAA standards.

Table 1-1 shows major HIPAA standards and compliance deadlines.

BUSINESS ASSOCIATES

HIPAA also affects many others in the health care field. For instance, outside medical billers are not CEs; they are not themselves required to comply with the law. However, they must follow HIPAA standards in order to do business with CEs. In HIPAA terms, they are **business associates (BA),** a category that includes:

> Law firms
> Accreditation agencies, such as the Joint Commission (JCAHO), an agency that evaluates and accredits nearly fifteen thousand health care organizations and programs
> Accountants
> Information technology (IT) contractors
> Medical transcription companies
> Independent contractors such as home-based medical coders, business office customer service staff members, and compliance consultants
> Collection agencies
> Third-party claim administrators (TPAs) hired by health plans to handle tasks like collecting premiums, keeping lists of members up to date, and processing and paying claims

HIPAA standards require CEs to have agreements with their business associates that ensure that these contractors will perform their work as required.

TABLE 1-1	HIPAA Administrative Simplification Compliance Timeline
DATE	**EVENT**
August 21, 1996	HIPAA
October 16, 2002	Compliance deadline for Electronic Health Care Transactions and Code Sets for all CEs except those that filed for an extension and are not a small health plan
April 14, 2003	Compliance deadline for Privacy Rule except for small health plans
October 16, 2003	Compliance deadline for Electronic Health Care Transactions and Code Sets for all CEs that filed for an extension and for small health plans
April 14, 2004	Compliance deadline for Privacy Rule for small health plans
July 30, 2004	Compliance deadline for Employer Identifier Standard for all CEs except small health plans
April 20, 2005	Compliance deadline for security standards for all CEs except small health plans
August 1, 2005	Compliance deadline for employer identifier standard for small health plans
April 20, 2006	Compliance deadline for security standards for small health plans
May 23, 2007	Compliance deadline for National Provider Identifier for all CEs except small health plans
May 23, 2008	Compliance deadline for National Provider Identifier for small health plans

HIPAA-Compliant?

Although some consultants say they have HIPAA-compliant material, the HHS website states that "some consultants and education providers have claimed that they or their materials or systems are endorsed or required by HHS, or by OCR. In fact, HHS and OCR do not endorse any private consultants'. . . materials or systems, and do not certify any persons or products as 'HIPAA compliant.'"

Staying Up to Date

HIPAA rules will continue to be issued and updated. Allied health professionals stay up to date via a number of means. Professional articles, conferences, and continuing education are all important. Listed below are the most important sources for updated information.

To learn about the latest HIPAA outreach materials and events, the HIPAA outreach listserv is ideal. To sign up, go to NIH at https://list.nih.gov/ and select HIPAA-OUTREACH-L under browse.

To be notified of developments by e-mail, subscribe to the HIPAA regulations (HIPAA-REGS) listserv by going to NIH and selecting "hipaa-regs" under browse.

FYI

Listserv

A listserv is an e-mail-based server that allows users to create, manage, and control electronic mailing lists on a network. The listserv manages list subscriptions, maintains archives of posted messages, optimizes mass mail delivery, and so forth. A listserv allows any networked user to subscribe to lists, receive list postings, query the listserv, set up a new list, access list archives, and more.

Figure 1-5

HHS Frequent Questions
Home Page

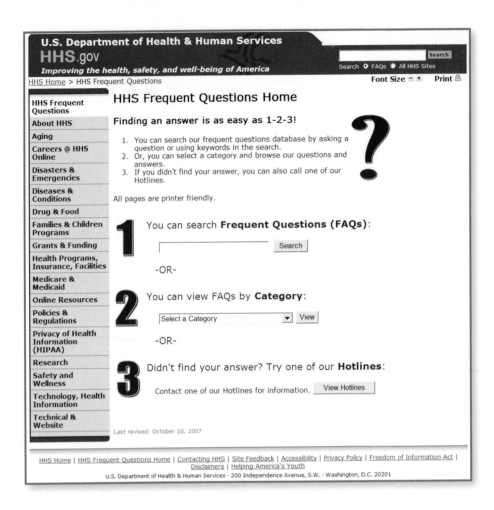

HIPAA FAQs are accessed via the HHS home page, clicking on Frequent Questions in the upper right corner, and then entering HIPAA in the first dialog box (see Figure 1-5).

Additional resources for various aspects of HIPAA are shown in Table 1-2.

1-3 Thinking It Through

Using the covered entity decision tree shown in Figure 1.4, decide whether each of the following is a covered entity or a business associate under HIPAA.

1. A billing service receives medical records electronically from a hospital, prepares health care claims, and mails the claims back to the hospital.

2. A consultant prepares a new office layout for a large physician practice.

3. A pharmacy receives written prescription orders from physicians and transmits billing information for patients who are Medicare Part D beneficiaries (the plan that covers the cost of the prescriptions) to Medicare via the Internet.

TABLE 1-2	HIPAA Resources
RESOURCE	**INTERNET ADDRESS**
The National Committee on Vital and Health Statistics (NCVHS) is a public advisory board to the secretary of Health and Human Services.	www.ncvhs.hhs.gov/
The Accredited Standards Committee (ASC X12) is responsible for the development and maintenance of electronic data interchange (EDI) standards for many industries. The X12 or insurance section of ASC X12 handles the EDI for the health insurance industry's administrative transactions. Under HIPAA, X12 standards have been adopted for most transactions between health plans and providers.	www.x12.org/
The National Council for Prescription Drug Programs (NCPDP) creates and promotes standards for the transfer of data to and from the pharmacy services sector of the health care industry. Under HIPAA, NCPDP standards were adopted for several retail pharmacy transactions.	www.ncpdp.org/
Designated Standard Maintenance Organizations (DSMO) are organizations designated by HHS to maintain the standards adopted under HIPAA Administrative Simplification. The current organizations serving as DSMOs are Accredited Standards Committee X12, Dental Content Committee of the American Dental Association, Health Level Seven, National Council for Prescription Drug Programs, National Uniform Billing Committee, and National Uniform Claim Committee.	www.hipaa-dsmo.org/
X12 implementation guides are specific technical instructions for implementing each of the adopted standards. The Implementation guides are prepared by X12 (as the standard maintainer) and are made available to the public for a modest fee by the Washington Publishing Company.	www.wpc-edi.com/ hipaa
Workgroup for Electronic Data Interchange (WEDI) fosters widespread support for the adoption of electronic commerce in health care.	www.wedi.org/
Strategic National Implementation Process (SNIP) is a collaborative health care industry process for the implementation of the HIPAA standards. This website includes white papers on transactions, security, identifiers, and privacy.	www.wedi.org/snip/
Medicare Electronic Data Interchange (EDI) is the official Medicare website that contains important information about how providers can electronically communicate with the Medicare program. This website contains EDI formats and instructions, transaction mapping information, statistics, FAQs about Medicare EDI, and other valuable EDI data.	www.cms.hhs.gov/ ElectronicBillingEDI Trans/01_overview. asp

CHAPTER REVIEW

CHAPTER SUMMARY

1. The Health Insurance Portability and Accountability Act (HIPAA) was passed to solve the problem of insurance coverage denials during job changes and to improve the efficiency and effectiveness of the health care industry by encouraging the use of electronic data interchange for health care transactions.

2. Title I of HIPAA, health insurance reform, provides additional rights for health insurance portability for individuals when they change jobs. Title II of HIPAA, the Administrative Simplification provisions, requires strict standards for the uniform transfer of electronic health care data such as for billing and payment, patients' rights regarding personal health information, and security rules that health care organizations must put in place to safeguard the confidentiality of patients' medical information.

3. Health insurance reform under Title I of HIPAA provides rights and protections for people covered by group health plans. The law limits exclusions for preexisting conditions; prohibits discrimination against employees and dependents based on their health status; and allows an opportunity to enroll in a new plan for individuals in certain circumstances. In some cases, it also provides the right to purchase individual coverage.

4. The five key provisions of HIPAA Administrative Simplification are (a) a requirement to establish standards for electronic health information transactions, (b) a mandate on providers and health plans to follow established standards and a timetable for doing so, (c) a requirement to establish privacy standards for health information, (d) the preemption of state law that is less strict than HIPAA standards, and (e) civil money penalties and prison for certain violations.

5. Under the concept of preemption, when there are two laws (in the case of HIPAA, one federal and the other state), the more stringent law applies: it preempts the less-rigid law.

6. The four areas in which standards under HIPAA Administrative Simplification have been legislated are (a) privacy standards, (b) security standards, (c) electronic transactions, and (d) enforcement.

7. The rule-making process is that (a) a proposed rule is drafted and then approved within the government; (b) the proposed rule, a document called Notice of Proposed Rule-Making (NPRM), is released for public comment; (c) the public has a period of time to provide comments; (d) HHS revises the rule and publishes the comments and reactions; and (e) the final rule is published, and the standards become effective twenty-four months after adoption

for most organizations (thirty-six months after adoption for small health plans).

8. A covered entity is an organization or a health care professional who (a) provides health care in the normal course of business and (b) electronically sends any information that is protected under HIPAA.

9. Covered entities are organizations or health care professionals such as health plans, providers, and clearinghouses. CEs contract with business associates, which are organizations and individuals such as law firms, accountants, and collection agencies that must follow the HIPAA policies and procedures of the CE with whom they have contracts.

10. To keep up with HIPAA standards and enforcement, allied health personnel rely on continuing education via professional publications and federal HIPAA outreach programs, using the major HIPAA resources for Internet updates in their interest areas.

MATCHING QUESTIONS

Match the key terms with their definitions.

d **1.** preemption

b **2.** Consolidated Omnibus Reconciliation Act (COBRA)

e **3.** covered entity

f **4.** business associate

g **5.** health plan

h **6.** provider

j **7.** clearinghouse

c **8.** Administrative Simplification

i **9.** direct provider

a **10.** Health Insurance Portability and Accountability Act of 1996

a. Broad federal law addressing the protection of health insurance when changing jobs and establishing standards for protecting medical information.

b. The federal law that Title I of HIPAA, health insurance reform, expands with additional continuation of coverage.

c. The name of Title II of HIPAA, which addresses the uniform transfer of electronic health care data as well as patient privacy protections.

d. Applying the more stringent law if federal and state laws differ.

e. Organization or health care professional who provides health care in the normal course of business and electronically sends information protected under HIPAA.

f. Entity that works under a contract for a covered entity and is therefore subject to the CE's HIPAA policies and procedures.

g. Insurance plan that provides or pays for medical care.

h. Organization or individual that furnishes, bills, or is paid for health care in the normal course of business.

i. Provider that has an immediate and primary relationship with patients.

j. Company that facilities electronic transactions such as insurance claims.

TRUE/FALSE QUESTIONS

Decide whether each statement is true or false.

_f_ 1. HIPAA was made law in order to increase federal revenues.

_t_ 2. Title I of HIPAA expands COBRA; Title II addresses administrative simplification.

_t_ 3. HIPAA Administrative Simplification standards cover privacy, security, electronic transactions, and enforcement.

_f_ 4. Under the HIPAA rule-making process, new standards have to be approved by a majority of the fifty states before becoming federal law.

_f_ 5. A covered entity has contracts to prepare taxes for a business associate.

_f_ 6. A provider is not a covered entity under HIPAA.

_f_ 7. Clearinghouses provide health care for their patients.

_f_ 8. Under the concept of preemption, state law always predominates over federal law.

_t_ 9. Electronic data interchange is the computer-to-computer exchange of routine business information.

_t_ 10. CMS stands for the Centers for Medicare and Medicaid Services.

MULTIPLE CHOICE QUESTIONS

Select the letter that best completes the statement or answers the question.

1. The HIPAA privacy standards are enforced by

   a. the Office for Civil Rights (OCR)

   b. the Centers for Medicare and Medicaid Services (CMS)

   c. the Department of Health and Human Services (HHS)

   d. the *Federal Register*

2. Federal laws are published in the

   a. local newspapers

   b. *Federal Register*

   c. NPRM

   d. HIPAA FAQs on the HHS home page

3. Covered entities are

   a. health plans, clearinghouses, and providers

   b. health plans, clearinghouses, and business associates

   c. clearinghouses, providers, and business associates

   d. health plans, providers, and business associates

4. Title II of HIPAA is known as

   a. COBRA

   b. health insurance reform

   c. NPRM

   d. Administrative Simplification

5. Hospitals, physicians, therapists, and nurses are examples of

   a. health plans

   b. providers

   c. clearinghouses

   d. business associates

6. Medicare, Medicaid, and TRICARE are examples of

   a. health plans

   b. providers

   c. clearinghouses

   d. business associates

7. Law firms, accountants, and medical transcription companies are examples of

   a. health plans

   b. providers

   c. clearinghouses

   d. business associates

8. A radiology clinic that transmits the results of radiological procedures to a physician is an example of

   a. a direct provider

   b. an indirect provider

   c. a clearinghouse

   d. a health plan

9. To be categorized as a covered entity, the organization or professional must _____ any HIPAA-protected information electronically.

   a. receive

   b. bill

   c. send (transmit)

   d. place on its website

10. Under the Administrative Simplification rule-making process, most organizations must comply with a new rule _____ after the law is adopted.

   a. within three years

   b. within two years

   c. within one year

   d. on the published effective date

SHORT ANSWER QUESTIONS

Answer the following questions.

1. List the four areas of HIPAA standards under Administrative Simplification.

   a. privacy standards

   b. security standards

   c. electronic transactions

   d. enforcement

2. List the three types of covered entities under HIPAA.

   a. health plans

   b. clearinghouses

   c. providers

APPLYING YOUR KNOWLEDGE

HIPAA Cases

1. Is an employer that does not provide on-site health care for its employees considered a covered entity?

2. Does HIPAA require a doctor who does not use computers in the office to buy them?

HIPAA Communications

A provider who sends electronic bills (health care claims) asked the following question. Read the question and the response, answering the questions below.

QUESTION

I'm a provider who bills electronically. Do I have to implement the HIPAA if I go back to submitting claims on paper?

RESPONSE

As a provider who bills electronically, you were required to comply with the HIPAA requirements of the Privacy Rule by April 14, 2003, unless, before that date, you stopped conducting any of the HIPAA transactions electronically. The HIPAA transactions commonly used by providers include claims, eligibility queries, claim status queries, and referrals. It is important to note that you cannot avoid the HIPAA requirements by hiring another entity, such as a billing service, to conduct these transactions electronically for you. While you and other health care providers could revert to conducting solely paper transactions, doing so would have many negative effects for most providers. The provider's business processes would be disrupted by having to prepare paper claims and check eligibility and claim status by phone. Reverting to paper would cause particular problems for those providers who receive Medicare payments. First, these providers would experience delays in receiving payments, because Medicare by law cannot pay paper claims until 28 days after receipt (as opposed to 14 days for electronic claims). Second, effective October 16, 2003, Medicare was prohibited by law from paying paper claims except for those from small providers and under certain other limited circumstances. After that date, any provider that does not meet the "small provider" or other exception would have to return to electronic claims submission in order to continue to receive Medicare reimbursement.

1. Is it possible for the provider in this case to avoid HIPAA compliance by using a medical billing service?

2. Are electronic claims paid more quickly or more slowly, according to the response?

RESEARCHING THE INTERNET

1. Access the Department of Labor home page at www.dol.gov/ebsa/faqs/faq_consumer_hipaa.html for frequently asked questions (FAQs) about COBRA provisions and HIPAA. What is the definition of a break in creditable coverage?

2. Explore the archives of the National Institutes of Health (NIH) HIPAA update listserv home page at HIPAA-OUTREACH-L @LIST.NIH.GOV. What were five topics discussed in a recent monthly archive?

3. It is important to use the Internet wisely. Using a search engine such as Google or Yahoo, locate these three websites:

   › Home page of the Office for Civil Rights, an agency of the Health and Human Services Department (HHS)

   › Home page of HIPAAcomply

   › Home page of HIPAAdvisory

Next, answer the following questions.

a. Authority

> Is the author identified?

> What are the author's credentials?

> Can you verify the credentials?

b. Purpose and coverage

> What is the address extension (.com, .edu, .gov, .org)?

> Can you identify the purpose of the site? What is it?

> Can you identify the depth of coverage? Is it comprehensive? Narrow?

c. Accuracy

> Was the page edited or reviewed by outside specialists?

> Are the facts correct, and are references cited?

> Based on your current level of knowledge of HIPAA, does the page seem credible?

d. Timeliness

> When was the site created?

> When was the site last updated?

e. Integrity of the information

> Are sources clearly labeled?

> Are references clearly cited?

> If pictures are used to convey information, is it possible that they were digitally enhanced or edited?

f. Objectivity or point of view

> Does a particular point of view come across?

> Does the site use inflammatory or provocative language?

> If there are advertisements on the page, are they easily differentiated from the actual page? Is there a connection between the advertisements and the webpage?

The HIPAA Privacy Standards

2

LEARNING OUTCOMES

After studying this chapter, you should be able to:

1. Briefly discuss the role of medical record documentation as the source of health information about patients.
2. List five responsibilities of covered entities under the HIPAA Privacy Rule.
3. Define protected health information (PHI).
4. Discuss the required content of the HIPAA Notice of Privacy Practices (NPP).
5. Discuss the privacy standards relating to appropriate release of PHI for treatment, payment, and operations (TPO) purposes.
6. Describe the conditions under which authorization for release of PHI must be obtained.
7. List the items that are essential for general authorizations to release information.
8. Discuss the major exceptions to the HIPAA release of information requirements.
9. State the privacy standards that relate to incidental use and disclosure of PHI.
10. State patients' rights regarding the use and disclosure of their PHI.

accounting of disclosures

Acknowledgment of Receipt of Notice of Privacy Practices

amendment

authorization

de-identified health information

designated record set (DRS)

disclosure

documentation

electronic medical record (EMR)

encounter

HIPAA Privacy Rule

hybrid record

incidental use and disclosure

medical record

medical standards of care

minimum necessary standard

Notice of Privacy Practices (NPP)

protected health information (PHI)

release of information (ROI)

subpoena

subpoena *duces tecum*

treatment, payment, and health care operations (TPO)

Why This Chapter Is Important

Patients' medical records—progress notes, reports, and other clinical materials—are legal documents that belong to the provider who created them. But the provider cannot withhold the *information* in the records unless providing it would be detrimental to the patient's health. The information belongs to the patient, who controls the amount and type of information that is released to others, except for the use of the data to treat him or her or to conduct the normal business transactions of the covered entity (with some legal exceptions).

Allied health personnel handle issues such as requests for information from patients' medical records. They need to know what information can be released about patients' conditions and treatments. What information can be legally shared among providers, health plans, and clearinghouses? What information must the patient specifically authorize for release? The answers to these questions are based on the HIPAA privacy standards.

Think about the following cases as you study the HIPAA privacy standards. In each case, no patient authorization for the action has been granted. Are the actions described HIPAA-compliant? Decide on your answers, and compare them with the case discussion that precedes the chapter summary.

CASE 1

A medical insurance specialist sends a patient's asthma history to the insurance company to resolve a claim that is being questioned.

CASE 2

A hospital pins patients' thank you letters to a bulletin board in the main lobby.

CASE 3

A hospital had treated a patient for a condition and identified the patient as having a very rare blood type. Now, another patient needs a donation of this blood type for essential surgery, but none is available in the regular blood supply. The hospital staff uses its database to identify and contact the patient with the rare blood type to ask for a blood donation.

The Medical Record

Allied health personnel regularly work with the **medical records** (charts) that providers create in physician practices, facilities, and clinics. These records contain facts, findings, and observations about patients' health history that are shared among health care professionals and nonclinicians to provide continuity of care. The records help in making accurate diagnoses of patients' conditions and in tracing the course of treatment.

> **Example** A primary care physician (PCP) creates a patient's medical record that contains the results of all tests ordered during an annual physical examination. To follow up on a problem that is noted, the PCP refers the patient to a cardiologist, also sending the pertinent data for that specialist's review. By studying the medical record, the cardiologist treating this referred patient learns the outcome of previous tests and avoids repeating them unnecessarily. Instead, he orders a needed test to be done on an outpatient basis at the hospital's radiology department, which also documents its results for interpretation by the cardiologist.

The process of creating medical records is called **documentation,** meaning organizing a patient's health record in chronological order using a systematic, logical, and consistent method. A patient's health history, examinations, tests, and results of treatments are all documented. Providers need complete and comprehensive documentation to show that they have followed the **medical standards of care** that apply in their state. Health care providers are liable (that is, legally responsible) for providing this level of care to their patients. The term *medical professional liability* describes this responsibility of licensed health care professionals.

Patients' medical records are legal documents. Good medical records are a part of the provider's defense against accusations that patients were not treated correctly. They clearly state who performed what service and describe why, where, when, and how it was done. Providers document the rationale behind their treatment decisions.

DOCUMENTING ENCOUNTERS

An **encounter** (also called a *visit*) is a direct personal contact between a patient and a provider in any place of service for the diagnosis and treatment of an illness or injury. Each encounter should be documented with the following minimum information:

> Patient's name

> Encounter date and reason

> Appropriate history and physical examination

> Review of all tests and drugs that were ordered

> Diagnosis

> Plan of care, or notes on procedures or treatments that were given

> Instructions or recommendations that were given to the patient

> Signature of the physician or other licensed health care professional who saw the patient

In physician practices, the medical record for a patient usually contains these data:

> The patient's unique identifying number in the practice's administrative system

> Biographical and personal information, including the patient's full name, date of birth, gender, race or ethnicity, residence address, marital status, identification numbers, home and work telephone numbers, and employer information, as applicable

> Copies of all communications with the patient, including letters, telephone calls, faxes, and e-mail messages; the patient's responses; and a note of the time, date, topic, and physician's response to each

> Copies of prescriptions and instructions given to the patient, including refills

> Original documents that the patient has signed, such as an advance directive

> Medical allergies and reactions, or their absence

> Up-to-date immunization record and history if appropriate, such as for a child

> Previous and current diagnoses, test results, health risks, and progress, including hospitalizations

> Copies of referral or consultation letters

> Records of any missed or canceled appointments

> Requests for information about the patient (from a health plan or an attorney, for example) and release data

For each hospital encounter, additional information is recorded:

> Type of encounter

> Date of encounter, including admission and discharge dates for inpatient admissions

> Physicians involved with the patient's care

> Patient's diagnoses and procedures

> Medications prescribed

> Disposition of the patient (that is, the arrangements for the next steps in the patient's care, such as transfer to a skilled nursing facility or to home and follow-up care or treatment)

Hospitals need complete patient information to support high-quality medical care, and the goal is typically a unit record that brings together all documented treatment information, both inpatient and outpatient, within a single facility. The flow of information into and out of the patient's medical record is typically funneled through a Master Person Index (MPI)—a master list of patients—that has a unique medical record number (MRN) for each patient. This same number is used whenever the patient has an encounter with the facility.

Figure 2-1 on page 30 shows an example of typical documentation.

PAPER, ELECTRONIC, AND HYBRID MEDICAL RECORDS

Medical records are created and stored on paper, electronically, or in some combination called a **hybrid record.** Because of the advantages, health care leaders in business and government are pressing for additional laws under HIPAA to require all providers to switch to **electronic medical records (EMR).** An electronic medical record—also called an electronic *health* record—is a collection of health information that provides immediate electronic access by authorized users. In electronic medical records, documentation may be created in a variety of ways, but all words and images are ultimately viewable on a computer screen.

Over the course of a lifetime, a patient may receive care from many different providers in physician offices, hospitals, emergency rooms, and home health settings. EMRs offer improved communications across the continuum of care from the primary care physician to the hospital to other locations of patient care. These advantages are summarized in Table 2-1 on page 31.

FYI

EMRs

The federal government, in Executive Order 13335, set the goal of using electronic records for all patients by 2014. However, due to cost, the need for technical support, and privacy and security concerns, adoption of electronic records will be gradual. For the near term, most hospitals and physician practices will have hybrid systems.

HIPAA Privacy: Protected Health Information

Given the huge amount of patient data stored by covered entities (refer to Chapter 1 for a definition), Congress recognized that a national *floor* of privacy protection was needed to protect it. The *HIPAA Standards*

Figure 2-1
Documentation Example

Ribielli, James E.
5/19/20--

CHIEF COMPLAINT: This 79-year-old male presents with sudden and extreme weakness. He got up from a seated position and became light-headed.

PAST MEDICAL HISTORY: History of congestive heart failure. On multiple medications, including Cardizem, Enalapril 5 mg qd, and Lasix 40 mg qd.

PHYSICAL EXAMINATION: No postural change in blood pressure. BP, 114/61 with a pulse of 49, sitting; BP, 111/56 with a pulse 50, standing. Patient denies being light-headed at this time.

HEENT: Unremarkable.

NECK: Supple without jugular or venous distension.

LUNGS: Clear to auscultation and percussion.

HEART: S1 and S2 normal; no systolic or diastolic murmurs; no S3, S4. No dysrhythmia.

ABDOMEN: Soft without organomegaly, mass, or bruit.

EXTREMITIES: Unremarkable. Pulses strong and equal.

LABORATORY DATA: Hemoglobin, 12.3. White count, 10.800. Normal electrolytes. ECG shows sinus bradycardia.

DIAGNOSIS: Weakness on the basis of sinus bradycardia, probably Cardizem induced.

TREATMENT: Patient told to change positions slowly when moving from sitting to standing, and from lying to standing.

John R. Ramirez, MD

COMPLIANCE TIP

45 CFR Parts 160 and 164

The HIPAA Privacy Rule is also often referred to by its number in the *Federal Register*, which is 45 CFR Parts 160 and 164.

for *Privacy of Individually Identifiable Health Information* rule is known as the **HIPAA Privacy Rule.** Enacted on April 14, 2003, the HIPAA privacy standards were the first comprehensive federal protection for the privacy of health information. These national standards protect individuals' medical records and other personal health information. Before the HIPAA Privacy Rule became law, the personal information stored in hospitals, physician practices, and health plans was governed by a patchwork of federal and state laws. Some state laws were strict, but others were not.

TABLE 2-1   **Advantages of Electronic Medical Records**

Immediate access to health information	The EMR is simultaneously accessible to all qualified users. Compared to sorting through papers in a paper folder, an EMR database can save time when vital patient information is needed. Once information is updated in a patient record, it is available to all who need access, whether across the hall or across town.
Computerized physician order management	Physicians can enter orders for prescriptions, tests, and other services at any time, along with the patient's diagnosis.
Clinical decision support	An EMR system can provide access to approved medical websites with the latest medical research to help medical decision making.
Automated alerts and reminders	The system can provide the staff with medical alerts and reminders to ensure that patients are scheduled for regular screenings and other preventive practices. Alerts can also be created to identify patient safety issues, such as possible drug interactions.
Electronic communication and connectivity	An EMR system can provide a means of secure and easily accessible communication between physicians and staff and in some offices between physicians and patients.
Patient support	Some EMR programs allow patients to access their medical records and request appointments. These programs also offer patient education on health topics and instructions on preparing for common medical tests, such as HDL cholesterol tests.
Administration and reporting	The EMR may include administrative tools, including reporting systems that enable facilities and medical practices to comply with federal and state reporting requirements.
Error reduction	An EMR can decrease medical errors that result from illegible chart notes, since notes are entered electronically on a computer or a handheld device. Nevertheless, the accuracy of the information in the EMR is only as good as the accuracy of the person entering the data; it is still possible to click the wrong button or enter the wrong letter.

The Privacy Rule says that covered entities must:

> Have privacy policies and procedures that are appropriate for their health care services

> Notify patients about their privacy rights and how their information can be used or disclosed

> Train employees so that they understand the privacy practices

> Appoint a privacy official responsible for seeing that the privacy policies and procedures are implemented

> Safeguard patients' records

COMPLIANCE TIP

Privacy Officers

The privacy official at a small physician practice may be the office manager, who also has other duties. At a large health plan, the position of privacy official may be full time.

In addition to electronic medical records that are used in medical offices and hospitals, many health care industry and government officials are encouraging the development of personal health records. An article from Family Practice Management (13, 5 [May 2006]: 57–62; www.aafp.org/fpm/20060500/57anin.html) related the way a PHR was used:

Meet Mrs. Johnson, a 79-year-old with diabetes, congestive heart failure and an electronic personal health record (PHR).

Mrs. Johnson saw her family physician this morning, and on the way home she realized she had already forgotten his instructions for her new heart medication. Was it two pills once a day, or did he say one pill twice a day? She also wondered when she would find out the results of the blood test he had ordered to determine her potassium level, which she struggles to keep normal. She was worried but knew that her online personal health record would enable her to find the answer to both questions as soon as she arrived home.

Once there, Mrs. Johnson sat down at her computer and logged in to the personal health record Web site that her family physician offered his patients. First, she sent a secure e-mail to her physician asking how to take her new medication. She was impressed to see that the new heart drug already was on her medication list. Next, Mrs. Johnson checked her in-box, where a message from her physician was waiting. Mrs. Johnson opened the message and was relieved to read that her potassium test had come back normal. Finally, she browsed the site's patient-education area and printed an article on potassium-rich diets before signing off.

The personal health record had informed and educated Mrs. Johnson. It also had saved her and her doctor's office from one or two follow-up phone calls. But its most important benefit on this day was still to come.

That evening, Mrs. Johnson woke with severe chest pain and shortness of breath. She was able to dial 911 and was rushed to the hospital. The emergency department physician diagnosed an acute coronary syndrome and started to write Mrs. Johnson's admission orders. He asked what medications she was taking. She could not remember all of them but told him that her entire medical record was available on the Internet. She gave him the password, which the physician used to access her online personal health record. There he found her medication list and her medication allergies, which included an aspirin allergy. He canceled the aspirin order he had just written and switched it to clopidogrel, signing, "a potential adverse drug event avoided, thanks to patient's PHR."

Based on this patient's history, what advantages can you cite for the use of PHRs? Are there any drawbacks to their use?

WHAT IS PROTECTED HEALTH INFORMATION?

The HIPAA Privacy Rule covers the use and disclosure of patients' **protected health information (PHI).** PHI is defined as individually identifiable health information that is transmitted or maintained by electronic media, such as over the Internet, or transmitted or maintained in any other form or medium. This information includes a person's:

> Name

> Address (including street address, city, county, ZIP code)

> Relatives' and employers' names

> Birth date

> Telephone numbers

> Fax number

> E-mail address

> Social Security number

> Medical record number

> Health plan beneficiary number

> Account number

> Certificate or license number

> Serial number of any vehicle or other device

> Website address

> Fingerprints or voiceprints

> Photographic images

HIPAA Exemptions

Certain benefits are always exempt from HIPAA, including coverage for accidents only, disability income coverage, liability insurance, workers' compensation, automobile medical payment and liability insurance, credit-only insurance (such as mortgage insurance), and coverage for on-site medical clinics.

Minimum Necessary Standard

When using or disclosing protected health information, a covered entity must try to limit the information to the minimum amount of PHI necessary for the intended purpose. The **minimum necessary standard** means taking reasonable safeguards to protect PHI from being accidentally released to those not needing the information during a correct use or disclosure.

Designated Record Set

Also, the covered entity only must release a designated record set, not all information. For purposes of the HIPAA Privacy Rule, *record* means any item, collection, or grouping of information that includes PHI and is maintained by a covered entity. The HIPAA term for a group of records is a **designated record set (DRS).** For a provider, the designated record set means the medical and billing records the provider maintains. It does not include appointment and surgery schedules, requests for lab tests, and birth and death records. It also does not include mental health information, psychotherapy notes, and genetic information, which are protected by more stringent release guidelines. For a health plan, the designated record set includes enrollment, payment, claim decisions, and medical management systems of the plan.

NOTICE OF PRIVACY PRACTICES AND ACKNOWLEDGMENT

According to the HIPAA privacy standards, covered entities must develop privacy policies and procedures to protect PHI.

Notice of Privacy Practices (NPP)

Covered entities must state their policies and procedures in a document called the **Notice of Privacy Practices (NPP).** They must also make their NPPs available on request to any person who requests them. If the CE is a health care provider with a physical service delivery site, it must have the notice available at the site for individuals to take with them.

CEs must also must give each patient a Notice of Privacy Practices at the first contact or encounter. For example, health plans must comply with specific requirements for notifying enrollees in their plans.

To meet this requirement, physician practices give patients their NPPs. The notice explains how patients' PHI may be used and describes their rights. Practices may choose to use a layered approach to giving patients the notice. On top of the information packet is a short notice, like the one shown in Figure 2-2, that briefly describes the uses and disclosures of PHI and the person's rights. The longer notice is placed beneath it.

If the first service delivery to an individual is electronic, the CE must provide the electronic notice automatically in response to the individual's first request for service. For example, the first time an individual requests a refill of a prescription through a covered Internet pharmacy, the pharmacy must respond with the pharmacy's Notice of Privacy Practices. Individuals who receive electronic notices have the right to obtain paper copies on request.

Acknowledgment of Receipt of Notice of Privacy Practices

Since providers must inform each patient about their privacy practices one time, it is important for HIPAA compliance to document this action. The most common method is to give the patient a copy of the NPP to read and then to have the patient sign a separate form called an **Acknowledgment of Receipt of Notice of Privacy Practices** (see Figure 2-3 on page 37). This form states that the patient has read the privacy practices and understands how the provider intends to protect the patient's rights to privacy under HIPAA.

The provider must make a good-faith effort to have patients sign this document. The provider must also document—in the medical record—whether the patient signed the form. The format for the acknowledgment is up to the provider.

> **EXAMPLE** A patient who has not received a privacy notice or signed an acknowledgment calls for a prescription refill. The office mails the patient a copy of the privacy notice, along with an acknowledgment of receipt form, and documents the mailing to show a good-faith effort that meets the office's HIPAA obligation in the event that the patient does not return the signed form.

Only a direct provider, one who directly treats the patient, is required to have patients sign an acknowledgment. An indirect provider, such

ABC Clinic   NOTICE OF PRIVACY PRACTICES
THIS NOTICE DESCRIBES HOW MEDICAL INFORMATION ABOUT YOU MAY BE USED AND DISCLOSED AND HOW YOU CAN GET ACCESS TO THIS INFORMATION. PLEASE REVIEW IT CAREFULLY.
WHY ARE YOU GETTING THIS NOTICE?
ABC Clinic is required by federal and state law to maintain the privacy of your health information. The use and disclosure of your health information is governed by regulations under the Health Insurance Portability and Accountability Act of 1996 (HIPAA) and the requirements of applicable state law. For health information covered by HIPAA, we are required to provide you with this Notice and will abide by this Notice with respect to such health information. If you have questions about this Notice, please contact our Privacy Officer at 877-555-1313. We will ask you to sign an "acknowledgment" indicating that you have been provided with this notice.

WHAT HEALTH INFORMATION IS PROTECTED?
We are committed to protecting the privacy of information we gather about you while providing health-related services. Some examples of protected health information are:
- .Information indicating that you are a patient receiving treatment or other health-related services from our physicians or staff;
- .Information about your health condition (such as a disease you may have);
- ..Information about health care products or services you have received or may receive in the future (such as an operation); or
- Information about your health care benefits under an insurance plan (such as whether a prescription is covered); when combined with:
- ..Demographic information (such as your name, address, or insurance status);
- ..Unique numbers that may identify you (such as your Social Security number, your phone number, or your driver's license number); and
- ..Other types of information that may identify who you are.

SUMMARY OF THIS NOTICE
This summary includes references to paragraphs throughout this notice that you may read for additional information.
1. **Written Authorization Requirement.** We may use your health information or share it with others in order to treat your condition, obtain payment for that treatment, and run our business operations. We generally need your written authorization for other uses and disclosures of your health information, unless an exception described in this Notice applies.
2. **Authorizing Transfer of Your Records.** You may request that we transfer your records to another person or organization by completing a written authorization form. This form will specify what information is being released, to whom, and for what purpose. The authorization will have an expiration date.
3. **Canceling Your Written Authorization.** If you provide us with written authorization, you may revoke, or cancel, it at any time, except to the extent that we have already relied upon it. To revoke a written authorization, please write to the doctor's office where you initially gave your authorization.
4. **Exceptions to Written Authorization Requirement.** There are some situations in which we do not need your written authorization before using your health information or sharing it with others. They include:
..*Treatment, Payment, and Operations.* As mentioned above, we may use your health information or share it with others in order to treat your condition, obtain payment for that treatment, and run our business operations.
..*Family and Friends.* If you do not object, we will share information about your health with family and friends involved in your care.
..*Research.* Although we will generally try to obtain your written authorization before using your health information for research purposes, there may be certain situations in which we are not required to obtain your written authorization.
..*De-identified Information.* We may use or disclose your health information if we have removed any information that might identify you. When all identifying information is removed, we say that the health information is "completely de-identified." We may also use and disclose "partially de-identified" information if the person who will receive it agrees in writing to protect your privacy when using the information.

Figure 2-2

Example of a Notice of Privacy Practices

..Incidental Disclosures We may inadvertently use or disclose your health information despite having taken all reasonable precautions to protect the privacy and confidentiality of your health information.

..Emergencies or Public Need. We may use or disclose your health information in an emergency or for important public health needs. For example, we may share your information with public health officials at the state or city health departments who are authorized to investigate and control the spread of diseases.

5. **How to Access Your Health Information.** You generally have the right to inspect and get copies of your health information.

6. **How to Correct Your Health Information.** You have the right to request that we amend your health information if you believe it is inaccurate or incomplete.

7. **How to Identify Others Who Have Received Your Health Information.** You have the right to receive an "accounting of disclosures." This is a report that identifies certain persons or organizations to which we have disclosed your health information. All disclosures are made according to the protections described in this Notice of Privacy Practices. Many routine disclosures we make (for treatment, payment, or business operations among others) will not be included in this report. However, it will identify many non-routine disclosures of your information.

8. **How to Request Additional Privacy Protections.** You have the right to request further restrictions on the way we use your health information or share it with others. However, we are not required to agree to the restriction you request. If we do agree with your request, we will be bound by our agreement.

9. **How to Request Alternative Communications.** You have the right to request that we contact you in a way that is more confidential for you, such as at home instead of at work. We will try to accommodate all reasonable requests.

10. **How Someone May Act on Your Behalf.** You have the right to name a personal representative who may act on your behalf to control the privacy of your health information. Parents and guardians will generally have the right to control the privacy of health information about minors unless the minors are permitted by law to act on their own behalf.

11. **How to Learn About Special Protections for HIV, Alcohol and Substance Abuse, Mental Health and Genetic Information.** Special privacy protections apply to HIV-related information, alcohol and substance abuse treatment information, mental health information, psychotherapy notes, and genetic information.

12. **How to Obtain a Copy of This Notice.** If you have not already received one, you have the right to a paper copy of this notice. You may request a paper copy at any time, even if you have previously agreed to receive this notice electronically. You can request a copy of the privacy notice directly from your doctor's office.

You may also obtain a copy of this notice from our website or by requesting a copy at your next visit.

13. **How to Obtain a Copy of Revised Notice.** We may change our privacy practices from time to time. If we do, we will revise this notice so you will have an accurate summary of our practices.

You will be able to obtain your own copy of the revised notice by accessing our website or by calling your doctor's office.

You may also ask for one at the time of your next visit. The effective date of the notice is noted in the top right corner of each page. We are required to abide by the terms of the notice that is currently in effect.

14. **How to File a Complaint.** If you believe your privacy rights have been violated, you may file a complaint with us or with the Secretary of the United States Department of Health and Human Services. To file a complaint with us, please contact our Privacy Officer.

No one will retaliate or take action against you for filing a complaint.

Figure 2.2

(*Continued*)

HIPAA for Allied Health Careers

Answer these questions based on the information in Figure 2-2.

1. What document is required when a patient asks ABC Clinic to transfer a record to another person or organization?
2. Is written authorization from a patient needed to use or disclose health information in an emergency?
3. What is the purpose of an accounting of disclosures?

Acknowledgment of Receipt of Notice of Privacy Practices

I understand that the providers of ABC Clinic may share my health information for treatment, billing, and health care operations. I have been given a copy of the organization's notice of privacy practices that describes how my health information is used and shared. I understand that ABC Clinic has the right to change this notice at any time. I may obtain a current copy by contacting the practice's office or by visiting the website at www.xxx.com.

My signature below constitutes my acknowledgment that I have been provided with a copy of the notice of privacy practices.

Signature of Patient or Legal Representative   Date _____

_____

If signed by legal representative, relationship to patient: _____

Figure 2-3

Sample Acknowledgment of Receipt of Notice of Privacy Practices

as a pathologist, must have a privacy notice but does not have to secure additional acknowledgments.

HIPAA does not require the parent or guardian of a minor to sign. If a child is accompanied by a parent or guardian who is completing other paperwork on behalf of the minor, it is reasonable to ask that adult to sign the acknowledgment of receipt. On the other hand, if the child or teen is unaccompanied, the minor patient may be asked to sign.

COMPLIANCE TIP

Keeping Acknowledgments on File

Providers must retain signed acknowledgments as well as documentation of unsuccessful attempts to obtain them for six years.

Disclosure of PHI

Under the HIPAA privacy standards, providers do not need specific authorization in order to use or disclose patients' PHI for treatment, payment, and operations (TPO) purposes, but they do need permission to release information for other reasons. *Use of PHI* means sharing or analysis *within* the entity that holds the information. **Disclosure** means the release, transfer, provision of access to, or divulging of PHI *outside* the entity holding the information.

RELEASE OF INFORMATION FOR TREATMENT, PAYMENT, AND OPERATIONS

Employees of covered entities follow a **release of information (ROI)** process to access PHI, prepare it for transmission, and send it to an individual or entity that has permission under HIPAA to obtain it.

Both use and disclosure of PHI are necessary for medical care, and so are permitted for **treatment, payment, and health care operations (TPO),** which are defined as follows:

› *Treatment:* This primarily consists of discussion of the patient's case with other providers. For example, a physician may document the role of each member of the health care team in providing care. Each team member then records actions and observations so that the ordering physician knows how the patient is responding to treatment.

› *Payment:* Providers usually submit claims to health plans on behalf of patients; this involves exchanging demographic and diagnostic information. Payment activities include determining insurance eligibility and coverage as well as billing and collections.

› *Operations:* This purpose includes activities such as accreditation (such as by the Joint Commission), staff training, and quality improvement.

Release by Any Method

Information for TPO can be released by using any method of communication, including in writing, orally, by fax, or by e-mail.

PHI Release to People Acting on a Patient's Behalf

A covered entity may release PHI to a family member, a relative, a friend, or other individuals who ask for the information on the behalf of the patient. The CE must have reasonable assurance that the person has been identified by the patient as being involved in his or her care. The CE can release this information if the patient does not object. Informal permission can be obtained by asking the patient. If the patient is not present or is incapacitated, the CE can make the disclosure if it is in the best interests of the patient.

> **Examples** A health plan discloses relevant PHI to a beneficiary's daughter who has called to assist her hospitalized elderly mother with a payment issue.
>
> A pharmacist dispenses filled prescriptions to a son picking up the items for his mother.

Although the HIPAA privacy standards permit sharing PHI for TPO purposes without authorization, they also require verification of the identity of the person who is asking for the information. The person's authority to access PHI must also be verified. If the requestor's right to the information is not certain, most covered entities follow a conservative policy that requires the patient to authorize the release of PHI.

COMPLIANCE TIP
Patient Sign-in Sheets

It is *not* a HIPAA violation to have a patient sign-in sheet at a facility's front desk.

COMPLIANCE TIP
Caller Identification of Provider

It is *not* a HIPAA violation if a provider's name appears on a patient's telephone caller ID.

Release of PHI About Minors

In general under the HIPAA privacy standards, a dependent child's PHI can be released to a parent. A covered entity may choose to provide or deny a parent access to a minor's personal health information if doing so is consistent with state or other applicable law and provided that the decision is made by a licensed health care professional. These options apply whether or not the parent is the minor's personal representative.

Because of a number of federal and state laws encouraging minors to get medical treatment without parental notification, PHI is often *not* released in these situations:

> The patient is an emancipated minor under the law

> The minor patient is married

> The treatment relates to the minor's pregnancy or child

> The treatment is for a sexually transmitted disease (STD), sexual assault, alcohol or drug abuse, or mental illness

Facility Directories

Many providers such as hospitals and skilled nursing care facilities maintain directories with patient contact information. A covered entity may informally secure patients' permission to have their names, general condition, religious affiliations, and locations in the facility directory. With this informal approval, the facility may disclose the patient's condition and location in the facility to anyone asking for that person by name and also may tell clergy about the patient's religious affiliation.

State Law on Consent

Although HIPAA does not require permission for use and disclosure of PHI for TPO, it does allow the covered entity to get the patient's authorization. Because some states have laws that preempt the federal HIPAA law by requiring this authorization, many covered entities follow the state law and ask patients to sign general forms that allow release.

RELEASE OF INFORMATION FOR PURPOSES OTHER THAN TPO

Many requests for information about patients are handled by health information management (HIM) and other medical office personnel. The requests coming from insurance companies, the media, or legal counsel vary in format; the ROI process requires each request to be evaluated from the HIPAA point of view.

The basic HIPAA privacy standard states that covered entities must have patients' authorization to use or disclose information that is not for TPO purposes. For example, a patient who wishes a provider to disclose PHI to a life insurance company must authorize this action.

HIPAA CAUTION

Consent Requirement Altered in HIPAA

The HIPAA Privacy Rule as first proposed contained an authorization requirement even for TPO. This was removed from the final rule because health care providers argued that it would interfere with patient care.

COMPLIANCE TIP

Health Care Providers and the Minimum Necessary Standard

The minimum necessary standard does not apply to any type of disclosure—oral, written, phone, fax, e-mail, or other—among health care providers for treatment purposes.

Authorization Is Required

The covered entity must have the patient sign a *general* **authorization** to release information that is not for treatment, payment, or operational purposes. Information about alcohol and drug abuse, sexually transmitted diseases (STDs), human immunodeficiency virus (HIV), and behavioral or mental health services may not be released without a *specific* authorization from the patient. The authorization document must be in plain language and include the following:

> A description of the information to be used or disclosed

> The name or other specific identification of the person(s) authorized to use or disclose the information

> The name of the person(s) or group of people to whom the covered entity may make the use or disclosure

> A description of each purpose of the requested use or disclosure

> An expiration date

> The signature of the individual (or authorized representative) and the date

In addition, the rule states that a valid authorization must include:

> A statement of the individual's right to revoke the authorization in writing

> A statement about whether the covered entity is able to base treatment, payment, enrollment, or eligibility for benefits on the authorization

> A statement that information used or disclosed after the authorization may be disclosed again by the recipient and may no longer be protected by the rule

A sample authorization form is shown in Figure 2-4.

Uses or disclosures for which the covered entity has received specific authorization from the patient do not have to follow the minimum necessary standard.

De-Identified Health Information

There are no restrictions on the use or disclosure of **de-identified health information** that neither identifies nor provides a reasonable basis for identifying an individual. For example, these identifiers must be removed: names, medical record numbers, health plan beneficiary numbers, device identifiers (such as pacemakers), and biometric identifiers, such as fingerprints and voiceprints.

Use of PHI in Marketing

HIPAA privacy standards require the covered entity to get prior authorization from individuals for using their PHI for marketing purposes. Under HIPAA law, *marketing* is defined as making a communication about a product or service that encourages the recipients of the communication to purchase or use the product or service.

Patient Name: _____

Health Record Number: _____

Date of Birth: _____

1. I authorize the use or disclosure of the above named individual's health information as described below.

2. The following individual(s) or organization(s) are authorized to make the disclosure: _____

3. The type of information to be used or disclosed is as follows (check the appropriate boxes and include other information where indicated)

☐ problem list
☐ medication list
☐ list of allergies
☐ immunization records
☐ most recent history
☐ most recent discharge summary
☐ lab results (please describe the dates or types of lab tests you would like disclosed): _____
☐ x-ray and imaging reports (please describe the dates or types of x-rays or images you would like disclosed): _____
☐ consultation reports from (please supply doctors' names): _____
☐ entire record
☐ other (please describe): _____

4. I understand that the information in my health record may include information relating to sexually transmitted disease, acquired immunodeficiency syndrome (AIDS), or human immunodeficiency virus (HIV). It may also include information about behavioral or mental health services, and treatment for alcohol and drug abuse.

5. The information identified above may be used by or disclosed to the following individuals or organization(s):

Name: _____

Address: _____

Name: _____

Address: _____

6. This information for which I'm authorizing disclosure will be used for the following purpose:

☐ my personal records
☐ sharing with other health care providers as needed/other (please describe): _____

7. I understand that I have a right to revoke this authorization at any time. I understand that if I revoke this authorization, I must do so in writing and present my written revocation to the health information management department. I understand that the revocation will not apply to information that has already been released in response to this authorization. I understand that the revocation will not apply to my insurance company when the law provides my insurer with the right to contest a claim under my policy.

8. This authorization will expire (insert date or event): _____

If I fail to specify an expiration date or event, this authorization will expire six months from the date on which it was signed.

9. I understand that once the above information is disclosed, it may be redisclosed by the recipient and the information may not be protected by federal privacy laws or regulations.

10. I understand authorizing the use or disclosure of the information identified above is voluntary. I need not sign this form to ensure health care treatment.

Signature of patient or legal representative: _____ Date: _____

If signed by legal representative, relationship to patient

Signature of witness: _____ Date: _____

Distribution of copies: Original to provider; copy to patient; copy to accompany use or disclosure

Note: This sample form was developed by the American Health Information Management Association for discussion purposes. It should not be used without review by the issuing organization's legal counsel to ensure compliance with other federal and state laws and regulations.

What specific information can be released

To whom

For what purpose

Figure 2-4

Sample Authorization Form

Activities that encourage use of a product or service but do not depend on individual PHI are not considered marketing under HIPAA. Messages that describe services or benefits are permitted with authorization, such as an updated list of physicians who participate in a particular health plan or a schedule of wellness classes at a hospital. HIPAA also permits communication about the patient's treatment, such as referrals to specialists, a general mailing to female patients advising them to have annual mammograms, and attendance at health fairs.

EXCEPTIONS TO DISCLOSURE STANDARDS

There are a number of exceptions to the usual rules for release:

> Court orders

> Workers' compensation cases

> Statutory reports

> Research

Release Under Court Order

If the patient's PHI is required as evidence by a court of law, the provider may release it without the patient's approval if a judicial order is received. In the case of a lawsuit, a court sometimes decides that a physician or medical practice staff member must provide testimony. The court issues a **subpoena,** an order of the court directing a party to appear and testify. If the court requires the witness to bring certain evidence, such as a patient medical record, it issues a **subpoena *duces tecum,*** which directs the party to appear, to testify, and to bring specified documents or items. If the provider cannot comply with the request, it is still important to respond to it.

Workers' Compensation Cases

State law may provide for release of records to employers in workers' compensation cases. The law may also authorize release to the state workers' compensation administration board and to the insurance company that handles these claims for the state.

Statutory Reports

Some specific types of information are required by state law to be released to state health or social services departments. For example, physicians must make statutory reports for patients' births and deaths and for cases of abuse. Because of the danger of harm to patients or others, communicable diseases such as tuberculosis, hepatitis, and rabies must usually be reported.

A special category of communicable disease control is applied to patients with diagnoses of human immunodeficiency virus (HIV) infection and acquired immunodeficiency syndrome (AIDS). Every state requires AIDS cases to be reported. Most states also require reporting of the HIV infection that causes the syndrome. However, state law varies concerning whether just the fact of a case is to be reported or if the patient's name must also be reported. The practice guidelines reflect the state laws and must be strictly observed, as all these regulations should be, to protect patients' privacy and to comply with the regulations.

Research Data

PHI may be made available to researchers approved by the CE. For example, if a physician is conducting clinical research on a type of diabetes, the practice may share information from appropriate records for analysis. When the researcher issues reports or studies based on the information, specific patients' names may not be identified.

Research subjects have the same rights as clinical care patients. That is, they can access the study's designated record set—most often a duplicate of the clinical record. They typically do not have the right to access the proprietary data of the study sponsor or any data that would compromise the integrity of the research.

Other Exceptions

Patients who are in the custody of correctional institutions or law enforcement personnel are another exception to the usual privacy standards for release of PHI without authorization. The covered entity can release information if law enforcement officers are investigating a crime or think that a patient is a crime victim. Likewise, PHI may be released for national security, intelligence, or other essential government purposes.

Psychotherapy Notes

Psychotherapy notes have special protection under HIPAA. According to the American Health Information Management Association Practice Brief on Legal Process and Electronic Health Records:

> Under the HIPAA Privacy Rule, psychotherapy notes are those recorded (in any medium) by a healthcare provider who is a mental health professional documenting or analyzing the content of conversation during a private counseling session or a group, joint, or family counseling session and that are separated from the rest of the individual's medical record. Notes exclude medication prescription and monitoring, counseling session start or stop times, the modalities and frequencies of treatment furnished, results of clinical tests, and any summary of diagnosis, functional status, the treatment plan, symptoms, prognosis, and progress to date. The privacy rule gives such notes extra protection, as may state law. (www.ahima.org.)

Psychotherapy notes cannot contain general notes, such as prescriptions, laboratory test results, or progress notes; they are the subjective notes of the psychiatrist. Summary information covering the patient's current mental state, medications, and other information needed for treatment or payment is regularly placed in the patient's medical records.

COMPLIANCE TIP

PHI and Answering Machines

If possible, ask patients during their initial visits whether staff members may leave messages on answering machines or with friends or family. If this is not done, messages should follow the minimum necessary standard; the staff member should leave a phone number and a request for the patient to call back—for example: "This is the doctor's office with a message for Mr. Warner. Please call us at 203-123-4567."

COMPLIANCE TIP

PHI and Reports

The American Association for Medical Transcription (AAMT) advises against using a patient's name in the body of a medical report. Instead, place data related to the patient's identification only in the demographic section of the report, where it can be easily deleted when the data are needed for research.

HIPAA CAUTION

Release of Psychotherapy Notes

A specific authorization by the patient is required for the release of psychotherapy notes.

State Statutes

Some state statues are more stringent than HIPAA specifications. Areas in which state statutes may differ from HIPAA include the following:

> Designated record set

> Psychotherapy notes

> Rights of inmates

> Information complied for civil, criminal, or administrative court cases

Each practice's privacy official reviews state laws and develops policies and procedures for compliance with the HIPAA Privacy Rule. The tougher rules are implemented.

INCIDENTAL USE AND DISCLOSURE

The privacy standards do not prohibit an **incidental use and disclosure,** meaning a release of PHI that happens as a result of (*incident to*) a correct use or disclosure.

Examples A provider instructs an administrative staff member to bill a patient for a particular procedure and is overheard by someone in the waiting room.

A health plan employee discussing a patient's health care claim on the phone is overheard by another employee who is not authorized to handle patient information.

If the provider and the health plan employee in these examples made reasonable efforts to avoid being overheard and reasonably limited the information shared, an incidental use or disclosure resulting from their conversations would be allowed under the Privacy Rule.

2-3   Thinking It Through

Based on your knowledge of the HIPAA Privacy Rule, do you think each of the following actions is compliant?

1. A medical insurance specialist does not disclose a patient's history of cancer on a workers' compensation claim for a sprained ankle. Only the information the recipient needs to know is given.

2. A physician's assistant faxes appropriate patient cardiology test results before scheduled surgery.

3. A physician sends an e-mail message to another physician requesting a consultation on a patient's case.

4. A hospital notifies a patient's adult child that his father has suffered a stroke and is in the intensive care unit.

Patients' Rights

Within the covered entity's designated record set, patients have the right to:

> Access, copy, and inspect their PHI

> Request amendments to their health information

> Obtain accounting of most disclosures of their health information

> Receive communications from providers via other means, such as sending a communication in a closed envelope but not on a postcard

> Complain about alleged violations of the regulations and the provider's own information policies

> Request restrictions on uses or disclosures of their PHI

Table 2-2 on page 46 reflects the principles on confidentiality of PHI from the American Medical Informatics Association (AMIA) and the American Health Information Management Association (AHIMA).

ACCESS, COPY, AND INSPECT

The covered entity must permit individuals to access, copy, and read their PHI held both by the CE and by any business associates. Access should generally be provided within thirty days. This period may be extended another thirty days by providing an explanation to the patient.

The CE may charge reasonable cost-based fees for copies of records. The fee may include only the cost of copying (including supplies and labor) and postage, if the patient requests that the copy be mailed. If the patient has agreed to receive a summary or explanation of protected health information, the CE may also charge a fee for preparation of the summary or explanation. The fee may not include costs associated with searching for and retrieving the requested information.

Various state laws also control the fees providers can charge a patient for copies of their medical records. Since a CE can charge only "reasonable" cost-based fees for providing medical records to patients, fees that are not cost-based, even if permitted by a state statute, may be contrary to the HIPAA regulation and thus preempted.

AMENDMENTS

An **amendment** is the correction of a finalized entry in a medical record that has been identified as incorrect. Corrections are in fact part of the medical record, so regular documentation guidelines must be followed when they are made. HIPAA requires covered entities to have a policy to meet HIPAA rules for accepting and processing patients' requests to amend their records. These guidelines require CEs to review and answer amendment requests within a thirty-day period if the records are accessible on-site, or within sixty days if stored off-site.

HIPAA CAUTION

Exceptions to Right of Access

An individual does not have the right to access psychotherapy notes or information complied in preparation for a civil, criminal, or administrative action or proceeding.

HIPAA CAUTION

Holding Records Hostage

Be sure that records are not being held hostage for balances due from patients for copying charges; this is a HIPAA violation.

TABLE 2-2	AMIA/AHIMA Principles on Confidentiality of PHI

- Inform individuals, through clear communications, about their rights and obligations and the laws and regulations governing protection and PHI use.

- Notify individuals in clear language about the organization's privacy practices and their rights in cases of breaches.

- Provide individuals with a convenient, affordable mechanism to inspect, copy, or amend their identified health information/records.

- Protect PHI confidentiality to the fullest extent prescribed under HIPAA, regardless of whether the organization and its employees all comply with HIPAA, state laws, and the policies and procedures in place to protect PHI.

- Use PHI only for legitimate purposes as defined under HIPAA or applicable laws.

- Prohibit PHI use for discriminatory practices, including those related to insurance coverage or employment decisions.

- Timely notification of individuals if security breaches have compromised the confidentiality of their PHI.

- Work with appropriate law enforcement to prosecute to the maximum extent allowable by law any individual or organization who intentionally misuses PHI.

- Continuously improve processes, procedures, education, and technology so PHI practices improve over time.

Source: American Medical Informatics Association and American Health Information Management Association Position Statement, quoted in *For the Record*, October 16, 2006.

Many CEs design an amendment form for patients to use. Some requests for amendment address factual matters, such as an incorrect birthday. Others, however, are more difficult to resolve because patients differ with the terminology used by the provider, which is essentially subjective and a professional judgment of the provider. Such issues are worked out through an amendment process.

The CE can deny a request for amendment if the item is accurate and complete, or if it is not part of the designated record set and would not be available for the patient's access under the Privacy Rule.

ACCOUNTING FOR DISCLOSURES

Patients have the right to an **accounting of disclosures** (see Figure 2-5) of their PHI. The list of disclosures does not have to include release:

❯ For TPO

❯ To the individual who is making the request (or to the individual's representative)

PATIENT REQUEST FOR ACCOUNTING OF DISCLOSURES

Patient Name	
Patient Address	
Medical Record #	Date of Birth
Name & Address of Requestor if not patient	

"Please consider this a request for an accounting of all disclosures for the time frames indicated below (Maximum time frame that can be requested is six years prior to the date of the request, but not before April 14, 2003). I understand that there is a fee for this accounting and wish to proceed. I understand that the accounting will be provided to me within sixty days unless I am notified in writing that an extension of up to thirty days is necessary."

Patient or Requestor to Complete:			Practice to Complete:		
From Date(s):	To Date(s):	Purpose of Disclosure:	Date Request In	Date Information to Patient	Fee

Date:	Signature of Patient or Legal Representative:
Date:	Signature of Patient or Legal Representative:

Figure 2-5
Patient Request for an Accounting of Disclosure

〉 For notification of or to persons involved in an individual's health care or payment for health care, for disaster relief, or for facility directories

〉 If the patient has signed an authorization to release the information

〉 Of a limited data set, such as for research

〉 For national security

〉 To correctional institutions or law enforcement officials

〉 Incident to otherwise correct release

When a patient's PHI is accidentally disclosed *externally*—to an outside person or organization—the disclosure should be documented in the individual's medical record, since the individual did not authorize it and it was not a permitted disclosure. An example is faxing a discharge summary to the wrong physician's office.

COMPLIANCE TIP

Incidental Use and Disclosure

Incidental disclosures do not have to be listed on an accounting of disclosures.

HIPAA does not require an accounting for *internal* inappropriate uses. However, if there is a chance that the disclosure could harm the patient, best practice is to notify the patient whose records have been released, explain what happened, and describe the steps that are being taken to handle it.

CONFIDENTIAL COMMUNICATIONS REQUIREMENTS

Patients have the right to ask covered entities to communicate with them in a way that is not the CE's usual procedure. For example, an individual may ask a provider to use a particular address or phone number, perhaps preferring contact at home or at the office. Health plans, specifically, must accommodate patients who indicate that disclosing their PHI could harm them and must follow their instructions for confidential communication.

PATIENT COMPLAINTS

Patients who observe privacy problems in their providers' offices can complain to the provider or the health plan, or to the Office for Civil Rights (OCR). Complaints to OCR must be in writing and sent either on paper or electronically, as described in Figure 2-6. They must be filed within 180 days of when the complainant knew or should have known that the act had occurred.

In addition, after the compliance dates above, individuals have a right to file a complaint directly with the covered entity. Individuals should refer to the covered entity's Notice of Privacy Practices for more information about how to file a complaint with the covered entity.

REQUESTS FOR RESTRICTIONS

A covered entity must permit an individual to ask the CE to restrict uses or disclosures of protected health information about the individual to carry out treatment, payment, or health care operations. A CE is not required to agree to a restriction. If the CE agrees to the restriction, it must honor this agreement unless the person needs emergency treatment that requires the disclosure.

2-4	Thinking It Through

Under the HIPAA privacy standards, does accounting for disclosure information include the following?

1. Release of the record for research purposes
2. Uses of the record by the nurse who is treating the patient
3. Releases authorized by the patient
4. Release of documentation to the patient's insurance company

U.S. Department of Health and Human Services • Office for Civil Rights HOW TO FILE A HEALTH INFORMATION PRIVACY COMPLAINT WITH THE OFFICE FOR CIVIL RIGHTS

If you believe that a person, agency or organization covered under the HIPAA Privacy Rule ("a covered entity") violated your (or someone else's) health information privacy rights or committed another violation of the Privacy Rule, you may file a complaint with the Office for Civil Rights (OCR). OCR has authority to receive and investigate complaints against covered entities related to the Privacy Rule. A covered entity is a health plan, health care clearinghouse, and any health care provider who conducts certain health care transactions electronically. For more information about the Privacy Rule, please look at our responses to Frequently Asked Questions (FAQs) and our Privacy Guidance. (See the web link near the bottom of this form.)

Complaints to the Office for Civil Rights must: (1) Be filed in writing, either on paper or electronically; (2) name the entity that is the subject of the complaint and describe the acts or omissions believed to be in violation of the applicable requirements of the Privacy Rule; and (3) be filed within 180 days of when you knew that the act or omission complained of occurred. OCR may extend the 180-day period if you can show "good cause." Any alleged violation must have occurred on or after April 14, 2003 (on or after April 14, 2004 for small health plans), for OCR to have authority to investigate.

Anyone can file written complaints with OCR by mail, fax, or email. If you need help filing a complaint or have a question about the complaint form, please call this OCR toll free number: 1-800-368-1019. OCR has ten regional offices, and each regional office covers certain states. You should send your complaint to the appropriate OCR Regional Office, based on the region where the alleged violation took place.

You can submit your complaint in any written format. We recommend that you use the OCR Health Information Privacy Complaint Form which can be found on our web site or at an OCR Regional office. If you prefer, you may submit a written complaint in your own format. Be sure to include the following information in your written complaint:

Your name, full address, home and work telephone numbers, email address.

If you are filing a complaint on someone's behalf, also provide the name of the person on whose behalf you are filing.

Name, full address and phone of the person, agency or organization you believe violated your (or someone else's) health information privacy rights or committed another violation of the Privacy Rule.

Briefly describe what happened. How, why, and when do believe your (or someone else's) health information privacy rights were violated, or the Privacy Rule otherwise was violated?

Any other relevant information.
Please sign your name and date your letter.

The following information is optional:

Do you need special accommodations for us to communicate with you about this complaint?
If we cannot reach you directly, is there someone else we can contact to help us reach you?
Have you filed your complaint somewhere else?

The Privacy Rule, developed under authority of the Health Insurance Portability and Accountability Act of 1996 (HIPAA), prohibits the alleged violating party from taking retaliatory action against anyone for filing a complaint with the Office for Civil Rights. You should notify OCR immediately in the event of any retaliatory action. . . .

If you require an answer regarding a general health information privacy question, please view our Frequently Asked Questions (FAQs). If you still need assistance, you may call OCR (toll-free) at: 1-866-627-7748. You may also send an email to OCRPrivacy@hhs.gov with suggestions regarding future FAQs. Emails will not receive individual responses.

Figure 2-6
OCR Privacy Rule Complaint Procedure

People also have the right to request that they be contacted at different places or in different ways. Patients may ask to be called at home rather than at the office, or to have written communications sent in an envelope rather than on a postcard. Patients also can opt out of facility directories; these individuals are called "no information" patients.

Case Discussion

At the beginning of the chapter, three cases were presented. They are reviewed below, with discussion about whether the actions were HIPAA-compliant.

CASE 1

A medical insurance specialist sends a patient's asthma history to the insurance company to resolve a claim that is being questioned.

Discussion: The use of the patient's medical record to handle a health care claim for payment purposes is compliant under the HIPAA privacy standards. It does not require the patient's authorization.

CASE 2

A hospital pins patients' thank you letters to a bulletin board in the main lobby.

Discussion: Unless the hospital, as the covered entity, had permission from the patients to display their letters, this use is potentially a violation of HIPAA. Best practice is to display this kind of communications from patients in a staff-only area.

CASE 3

A hospital had treated a patient for a condition and identified the patient as having a very rare blood type. Now, another patient needs a donation of this blood type for essential surgery, but none is available in the regular blood supply. The hospital staff uses its database to identify and contact the patient with the rare blood type to ask for a blood donation.

Discussion: This action is HIPAA-compliant because the information is being sought for treatment purposes.

CHAPTER REVIEW

CHAPTER SUMMARY

1. Allied health personnel work with medical records daily. Records contain health information about patients and are used to show that the proper medical standard of care was provided. Encounters must be documented in a standard way so that key information is always available to covered entities.

2. The HIPAA Privacy Rule requires covered entities to (a) have a set of privacy policies and procedures that are appropriate for its health care services, (b) notify patients about their privacy rights and how their information can be used or disclosed, (c) train employees so that they understand the privacy practices, (d) appoint a privacy official responsible for seeing that the privacy policies and procedures are implemented, and (e) safeguard patients' records.

3. Protected health information (PHI) is defined as individually identifiable health information that is transmitted or maintained by electronic media, such as over the Internet, by computer modem, or on magnetic tape or compact disks.

4. The HIPAA Notice of Privacy Practices (NPP) must contain an explanation of the policies and procedures a covered entity has in place to protect PHI. The NPP must describe the type of information that is protected, under what conditions it will be released, exceptions to these conditions, and patients' rights.

5. Release of PHI for treatment, payment, and operations (TPO) purposes is permitted under HIPAA. Treatment involves communications regarding the patient's health care. Payment involves communications between providers and health plans. Operations include communications that are necessary for the normal functioning of the covered entity.

6. The basic HIPAA privacy standard states that covered entities must have the authorization of patients to release their PHI other than for TPO purposes.

7. General authorizations to release information must include:
   › A description of the information to be used or disclosed
   › The name or other specific identification of the person(s) authorized to use or disclose the information
   › The name of the person(s) or group of people to whom the covered entity may make the use or disclosure
   › A description of each purpose of the requested use or disclosure
   › An expiration date
   › The signature of the individual (or authorized representative) and the date

> A statement of the individual's right to revoke the authorization in writing

> A statement about whether the covered entity is able to base treatment, payment, enrollment, or eligibility for benefits on the authorization

> A statement that information used or disclosed after the authorization may be disclosed again by the recipient and may no longer be protected by the rule

8. Exceptions to the HIPAA release of information requirements include release under court order, in workers' compensation cases, for statutory reports, for research, to law enforcement or correctional institution personnel, and in cases where other state standards are more stringent than HIPAA. Psychotherapy notes have special protection.

9. Incidental use and disclosure of PHI is not prohibited under HIPAA.

10. Patients have the following rights regarding the use and disclosure of their PHI: (a) to access, copy, and inspect their PHI; (b) to request amendments to their health information; (c) to obtain accounting of most disclosures of their health information; (d) to receive communications from providers via other means; (e) to complain about alleged violations of the regulations and the provider's own information policies; and (f) to request restrictions on uses or disclosures of their PHI.

MATCHING QUESTIONS

Match the key terms with their definitions.

 1. accounting of disclosures

 2. authorization

3. de-identified health information

4. incidental use and disclosure

 5. minimum necessary standard

6. protected health information (PHI)

 7. release of information (ROI)

8. treatment, payment, and health care operations (TPO)

a. A patient's written approval to release PHI.

b. Health information from which all individual identifying data have been removed.

c. Accidental use or disclosure that occurs during a correct use or disclosure.

d. Sharing a patient's protected health information with another entity.

e. Under HIPAA, the three purposes for which PHI may be released without authorization.

h   **9.** amendment

g   **10.** documentation

f. A list of ROI of their PHI that patients can ask to review.

g. A chronological record of a patient's health care.

h. A patient's requested alteration of an item in the medical record.

i. Under HIPAA, the principle of releasing only PHI that is pertinent for the purpose.

j. Individually identifiable health information that is transmitted or maintained electronically.

TRUE/FALSE QUESTIONS

Decide whether each statement is true or false.

t   **1.** Encounters with patients are documented by providers to help make accurate diagnoses and provide continuity of care among health care professionals.

f   **2.** Hybrid records combine physician office and hospital documentation.

t   **3.** Under the HIPAA privacy standards, covered entities must have privacy policies and procedures in place.

t   **4.** Protected health information includes any data that identify individuals.

f   **5.** Providers' groups of records are called de-identified health information.

t   **6.** Providers that have a physical service site, like an office, must make their Notice of Privacy Practices available at that site.

f   **7.** If a patient does not sign an Acknowledgment of Receipt of NPP, the provider cannot treat the individual.

f   **8.** Minors are not allowed to sign Acknowledgments of Receipt of NPPs.

f   **9.** Providers cannot send patients' protected health information to health plans without a signed authorization.

t   **10.** With reasonable confidence that a patient has identified another person as being involved with his or her care, a covered entity can release the patient's PHI to that person.

MULTIPLE CHOICE QUESTIONS

Select the letter that best completes the statement or answers the question.

1. What is included in protected health information under HIPAA?

   a. the patient's address

   b. the patient's allergies

   c. the patient's medical record number

   d. all of the above

2. What is protected under the HIPAA privacy standards?

   a. patient data that are printed and mailed

   b. patient information sent by e-mail

   c. patient information communicated over the phone

   d. all of the above

3. A patient's authorization to release information is needed

   a. in most situations when PHI will be shared other than for treatment, payment, or operations purposes

   b. upon hospital admission

   c. when patient information is used for billing the patient's health plan

   d. when patient information is to be shared with another clinician who will treat the patient

4. What does not have to be included in an accounting of disclosures?

   a. releases of the record for research purposes

   b. use of the record by treating physicians

   c. releases that the patient has authorized

   d. all of the above

5. Patients always have the right to

   a. withdraw their authorization to release information

   b. alter the information in their medical records

   c. block release of information about their communicable diseases to the state health department

   d. none of the above

6. The authorization to release information must specify

   a. the number of pages to be released

   b. the Social Security number of the patient

   c. the entity to whom the information is to be released

   d. the name of the treating physician

7. Health information that does not identify an individual is referred to as

   a. protected health information

   b. authorized health release

   c. statutory data

   (d.) de-identified health information

8. Under the HIPAA Privacy Rule, covered entities must

   a. train employees about the CE's privacy policy

   b. appoint a staff member as the privacy officer

   (c.) both a and b

   d. neither a nor b

9. A Notice of Privacy Practices is given to

   (a.) patients

   b. business associates

   c. other covered entities

   d. none of the above

10. Patients' PHI may be released without authorization to

    a. local newspapers

    (b.) employers in workers' compensation cases

    c. social workers

    d. family and friends

SHORT ANSWER QUESTIONS

Answer the following questions.

1. Define the following abbreviations.

   a. NPP _notice of privacy practices_

   b. PHI _personal health information_

   c. TPO _treatments, payments, + health care operations_

2. List five responsibilities of covered entities under the HIPAA Privacy Rule.

   Have policies + procedures that are appropriate for their health care service
   notify patients about their rights + how their info can be used or disclosed
   Train employees so that they understand the privacy practices.
   Safeguard patients records
   Appoint a privacy official responsible for seeing that the privacy
   Policies + procedures are implemented.

APPLYING YOUR KNOWLEDGE

HIPAA Cases

1. In each of these cases of release of PHI, was the HIPAA Privacy Rule followed?

   a. A laboratory communicates a patient's medical test results to a physician by phone.

   b. A physician mails a copy of a patient's medical record to a specialist who intends to treat the patient.

   c. A hospital faxes a patient's health care instructions to a nursing home to which the patient is to be transferred.

   d. A doctor discusses a patient's condition over the phone with an emergency room physician who is providing the patient with emergency care.

   e. A doctor orally discuss a patient's treatment regimen with a nurse who will be involved in the patient's care.

   f. A physician consults with another physician about a patient's condition by e-mail.

   g. A hospital faxes an organ donor's medical information to another hospital that is treating the organ recipient.

   h. A medical insurance specialist answers questions over the phone from a health plan about the dates of service on a submitted claim.

2. A nineteen-year-old has registered for a physician visit using an insurance card listing him as a qualified dependent on a parent's health plan. Later, the parents call the practice to find out why their child saw the physician. The age of majority in the state is eighteen. Is releasing any information beyond verifying the patient's visit a HIPAA-compliant action?

3. Two doctors are having a confidential conversation about a patient's condition in the hall of the hospital. Someone visiting another patient accidentally overhears their conversation. Is this a HIPAA privacy standard violation?

HIPAA Communications

Angelo Diaz signed the authorization form below. When his insurance company called for an explanation of a reported procedure that Dr. Handlesman performed to treat a stomach ulcer, George Welofar, the clinic's registered nurse, released copies of his complete file. On reviewing Mr. Diaz's history of treatment for alcohol abuse, the insurance company refused to pay the claim, stating that Mr. Diaz's alcoholism had caused the condition. Mr. Diaz complained to the practice manager about the situation.

Should the information have been released?

Patient Name: Angelo Diaz

Health Record Number: ADI00

Date of Birth: 10-12-1945

1. I authorize the use or disclosure of the above named individual's health information as described below.

2. The following individual(s) or organization(s) are authorized to make the disclosure: Dr. L. Handlesman

3. The type of information to be used or disclosed is as follows (check the appropriate boxes and include other information where indicated)

☐ problem list
☐ medication list
☐ list of allergies
☐ immunization records
☑ most recent history
☐ most recent discharge summary
☐ lab results (please describe the dates or types of lab tests you would like disclosed): _____
☑ x-ray and imaging reports (please describe the dates or types of x-rays or images you would like disclosed): _____
☐ consultation reports from (please supply doctors' names): _____
☐ entire record
☑ other (please describe): Progress notes

4. I understand that the information in my health record may include information relating to sexually transmitted disease, acquired immunodeficiency syndrome (AIDS), or human immunodeficiency virus (HIV). It may also include information about behavioral or mental health services, and treatment for alcohol and drug abuse.

5. The information identified above may be used by or disclosed to the following individuals or organization(s):

Name: Blue Cross & Blue Shield

Address: _____

Name: _____

Address: _____

6. This information for which I'm authorizing disclosure will be used for the following purpose:

☐ my personal records
☐ sharing with other health care providers as needed/other (please describe): _____

7. I understand that I have a right to revoke this authorization at any time. I understand that if I revoke this authorization, I must do so in writing and present my written revocation to the health information management department. I understand that the revocation will not apply to information that has already been released in response to this authorization. I understand that the revocation will not apply to my insurance company when the law provides my insurer with the right to contest a claim under my policy.

8. This authorization will expire (insert date or event): _____

If I fail to specify an expiration date or event, this authorization will expire six months from the date on which it was signed.

9. I understand that once the above information is disclosed, it may be redisclosed by the recipient and the information may not be protected by federal privacy laws or regulations.

10. I understand authorizing the use or disclosure of the information identified above is voluntary. I need not sign this form to ensure healthcare treatment.

Signature of patient or legal representative: Angelo Diaz   Date: 3-1-2008

If signed by legal representative, relationship to patient

Signature of witness: _____   Date: _____

Distribution of copies: Original to provider; copy to patient; copy to accompany use or disclosure

Note: This sample form was developed by the American Health Information Management Association for discussion purposes. It should not be used without review by the issuing organization's legal counsel to ensure compliance with other federal and state laws and regulations.

RESEARCHING THE INTERNET

1. Access the **HIPAA FAQs** website of the Office for Civil Rights at www.hhs.gov/hipaafaq/ and answer these questions.
    Can a physician practice use reception-area sign-in sheets?
    Do authorizations have to be in writing?

2. On the same website, research and report on HIPAA and minors, covering what happens when an individual reaches the age of majority and who controls **PHI** about health care services provided when the individual was a minor.

3. Access the website of the Health Privacy Project at www. healthprivacy.org, and visit the state law page. Research the law in your state. Assign team members to compare and contrast various aspects of HIPAA privacy standards with state law.

The HIPAA Security Standards

3

CHAPTER OUTLINE

LEARNING OUTCOMES

After studying this chapter, you should be able to:

1. Define electronic protected health information (ePHI).
2. List the three goals of the HIPAA security standards.
3. Compare and contrast risk analysis and risk management.
4. Define identity theft.
5. Describe the organization of the HIPAA Security Rule.
6. Explain the purpose of implementation specifications, distinguishing between those that are required and those that are addressable.
7. Describe key administrative safeguards.
8. Discuss key physical safeguards.

9. Describe key technical safeguards.
10. Discuss the HIPAA security considerations for portable and/or mobile devices and for fax and e-mail transmissions.

KEY TERMS

addressable implementation specifications
administrative standards
antivirus software
authentication
authorization
availability
backup procedure
confidentiality
confidentiality notice
cryptography
degaussing
digital certificate
e-discovery
electronic protected health information (ePHI)
encryption
firewall
HIPAA Security Rule
identity theft

implementation specifications
integrity
malware
network security
password
physical standards
portable and/or mobile media devices
protocol
required implementation specifications
risk analysis
risk management
role-based authorization
sanction policy
security incidents
technical standards
unique user identification
workstation

>> **Why This Chapter Is Important**

The HIPAA security standards complement the HIPAA privacy regulations by describing how electronic information about patients must be kept safe. Knowledge of the security measures is essential for allied health personnel, who must know how to safeguard the electronic exchange of information on behalf of patients.

Think about the following cases as you study the HIPAA security standards. In each case, protected health information had been improperly disclosed. In your opinion, what steps could have been taken to avoid the security violation? Decide on your answers, and compare them with the case discussion that precedes the chapter summary.

CASE 1

A medical assistant e-mailed the results of a patient's TB test to the wrong specialist's office.

CASE 2

The Department of Veterans Affairs announced that all agency computers would be upgraded with data security encryption immediately. The move came in the wake of a second theft of a VA laptop from a vendor's office. Laptops would be the first to receive the encryption programs, followed by desktop computers and portable media.

CASE 3

A thief stole backup tapes from the van of a provider's employee who had taken the tapes in order to do some work over the weekend. The provider waited for more than three weeks to tell the state department of justice and the patients about the loss of personal medical and financial information. The provider was later ordered by the state to provide twelve months of free credit monitoring to patients affected by the data breach. The provider also had to pay patient claims for any losses directly resulting from the data theft.

HIPAA Security

The **HIPAA Security Rule** was published in the *Federal Register* on February 20, 2003, with required implementation by April 20, 2005. The rule contains many security standards that have become federal law, as required under HIPAA. The security standards require appropriate administrative, physical, and technical safeguards to protect the privacy of protected health information against unintended disclosure through breach of security (see Figure 3-1 on page 62).

ELECTRONIC PROTECTED HEALTH INFORMATION

Like the HIPAA Privacy Rule, the Security Rule applies to covered entities (CEs; see Chapter 1). The Security Rule, though, focuses only on *electronic* protected health information, not on paper records. **Electronic protected health information (ePHI)** is PHI (see Chapter 2) that is stored or transmitted in electronic form. Electronic storage includes computer systems and storage devices of all types. Electronic transmission methods include Internet, computer networks within organizations, and

Figure 3-1

HIPAA Security Standard
Home Page

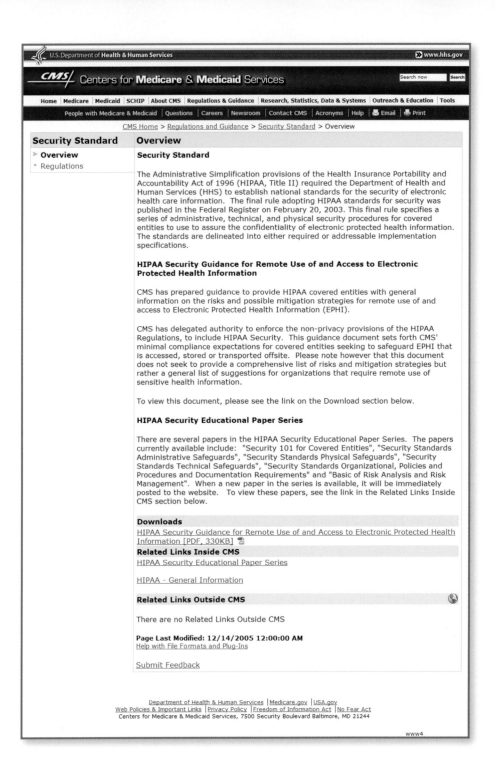

ePHI that is physically moved from one location to another using magnetic tape, disks, CDs, flash drives, or any other removable media.

The goals of the HIPAA security standards (see Figure 3-2) are to ensure:

〉 The **confidentiality** of ePHI—ensuring that the information is shared only among authorized individuals or organizations

〉 The **integrity** of ePHI—making sure that the information is not changed in any way during storage or transmission and that it is

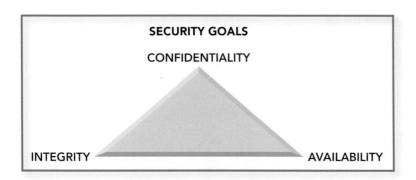

Figure 3-2
Security Goals

authentic and complete and can be relied on to be sufficiently accurate for its purpose

> The **availability** of ePHI—ensuring that the systems responsible for delivering, storing, and processing data are accessible, when needed, by those who need them under both routine and emergency circumstances

The HIPAA security standards do not state specific actions that CEs must take. Instead, the rule recognizes that the policies and procedures must vary according to the size of a CE (the number of employees and locations) and the type of work it performs. The wording of the security standards provides goals and examples that allow a covered entity to use any security measures that allow it to meet the requirements. A CE must determine which security measures and specific technologies are reasonable and appropriate for implementation in its organization.

THREATS TO INFORMATION SECURITY

The HIPAA security standards require covered entities to analyze and then manage the risk that any ePHI they possess could be accessed by anyone other than appropriate and authorized individuals. **Risk analysis** means that the CE must examine and document any potential threats to the security of its information. **Risk management** means establishing policies and procedures that reduce the risk of breaches of security. The risk analysis and management process involves planning, implementing, and verifying the protection of the CE's electronic assets from internal and external threats.

Threats to information security come from a number of sources, including natural events as well as events resulting from intent to cause harm. Common threats include:

> Natural disasters such as rain, fire, flood, earthquake, explosion, lightning, and building structural failure

> Utility outages such as loss of electrical power

> **Malware**—any program that harms information systems, which is often brought into an organization through e-mail attachments or programs that are downloaded from the Internet (see Table 3-1)

> Identity theft

> Subversive employees or contractors

> Computer system changes and updates

COMPLIANCE TIP

Ongoing Tasks

Covered entities must ensure that the risk analysis and risk management process is ongoing and dynamic and can change as the environment or operations change.

TABLE 3-1	Types of Malware
Viruses	A virus self-replicates by inserting copies of itself into host programs or data files. Viruses are often triggered through user interaction, such as opening a file or running a program.
Worms	A worm is a self-replicating, self-contained program that usually executes itself without user intervention.
Trojan Horses	A Trojan horse is a self-contained, nonreplicating program that, while appearing to be benign, actually has a hidden malicious purpose. Trojan horses either replace existing files with malicious versions or add new malicious files to systems. They often deliver other attacker tools to systems.
Malicious Mobile Code	Malicious mobile code is software with malicious intent that is transmitted from a remote system to a local system and then executed on the local system, typically without the user's explicit instruction.
Blended Attacks	A blended attack uses multiple infection or transmission methods. For example, a blended attack could combine the propagation methods of viruses and worms.
Tracking Cookies	A tracking cookie is a persistent cookie that is accessed by many websites, allowing a third party to create a profile of a user's behavior. Tracking cookies are often used in conjunction with web bugs, which are tiny graphics on websites that are referenced within the HTML content of a webpage or e-mail. The only purpose of the graphic is to collect information about the user viewing the content.
Attacker Tools	Various types of attacker tools might be delivered to a system as part of a malware infection or other system compromise. These tools allow attackers to have unauthorized access to or use of infected systems and their data, or to launch additional attacks.
Non-malware Threats	These are often associated with malware. Phishing uses computer-based means to trick users into revealing financial information and other sensitive data. Phishing attacks frequently place malware or attacker tools on systems.

It is often difficult for individuals to recognize when a computer system has suffered a security compromise. The job of detecting problems in each CE's electronic system is shared by personnel who use the ePHI in their daily work and personnel such as information technology specialists who monitor and service the computer system.

SECURITY BACKGROUND

Because of the advantages to health care organizations, most CEs use computer networks rather than providing every employee with a

HIPAA for Allied Health Careers

stand-alone personal computer. The CE's information is accessed and stored on devices connected over this network, permitting employees to share data and programs. The network is connected to larger networks outside the organization, such as the Internet. As a result, **network security,** the practice of protecting and preserving resources and information on a network, is an important information security issue. Maintaining a secure network involves a variety of different aspects.

Network Basics

Within an organization, PCs are connected to a network so that users can exchange and share information and hardware (such as printers). The central component of the network is a server, a powerful computer that acts as an intermediary between PCs on the network and provides a large volume of disk storage for shared information, such as shared application programs. The server controls access to the data through the use of access controls that limit user access to various files and programs stored on the server.

Imagine that all of a facility's computer resources are placed in locked rooms—accounting data in one room, research in another room, and so on. Decisions need to be made about who will have access rights to the different types of data. Once access rights have been assigned, each user is given a key to the designated rooms. To initiate a session on the network, users at a PC must log into the server and provide a user ID and key (a password). They are then able to use the files to which they have been granted access rights. In addition to assigning access rights, CEs use software to create activity logs. These logs detail the activity on each system and can be reviewed for abnormalities.

Routers, Firewalls, and Proxy Servers

A router is a device that links a local network to a remote network and determines the best route for data to travel across the network. For example, a company may use a router to connect a local area network to the Internet. A network router reads every packet of data passed to it, determining whether it is intended for a destination within the router's own network or should be passed farther along the Internet.

Depending on the configuration, the packets of data usually must pass through an open port in the firewall before continuing on to their destination. A **firewall** is a security device that examines traffic entering and leaving a network and determines (based on a set of user-defined rules) whether to forward it toward its destination. Packet filtering is a process in which a firewall examines the nature of each piece of information traveling into or out of the network. A firewall acts as a gatekeeper, deciding who has legitimate access to a network and what sorts of materials should be allowed in and out.

The purpose of a firewall is not only to prevent unauthorized entry into the network, but also to prevent unauthorized data from exiting the network. It controls what users can access on the Internet. For example, a firewall could be set up to block access to websites that are used for playing games. Firewalls are also used to log information such

as files that are transferred, websites that are visited, and servers that are logged into. Some firewalls even have antivirus software built in to reject known viruses.

Passwords

Passwords are another means of preventing unauthorized users from gaining access to information on a computer or network. Password utilization is a standard practice in most health care organizations. It is easy to implement, and it can keep unauthorized users from successfully logging onto a system or network. Password logging programs can track all successful and failed log-in attempts, which can be useful in detecting possible break-in attempts or unauthorized logging.

Unless they are very small organizations, most CEs use **role-based authorization,** in which access is based on the individual's title and/or job function, so that only people who need information can see it. Once access rights have been assigned, each user is given a key to the designated databases. Users must enter a user ID and a key to see files to which they have been granted access rights. For example, in a hospital admissions department, receptionists may view the names of patients being admitted that day, but they should not see those patients' medical records. However, the nurse or physician needs to view the patient records. Receptionists are given individual computer passwords that let them view the day's schedule but that deny entry to patient records. The physicians and nurses possess computer passwords that allow them to see all patient records.

Cryptography and Transmission Protocols

Cryptography is the protection of information by transforming it into an unreadable format before it is distributed. To read a message, the recipient must have a key that deciphers the information. The act of encoding the contents of the message is known as **encryption.** Cryptography also enables the recipient to determine whether the message has been intercepted and tampered with before final delivery. This allows the message to be checked for authenticity.

There are two types of encryption. In symmetric encryption, the same key is used to encrypt and decrypt the message. In asymmetric (or public-key) encryption, one key encrypts a message and another decrypts it.

Another method, based on data communication technology, uses a network communication **protocol** to ensure that the data sent are the data received. This requires a kind of check digit at the beginning and end of a message that is recognized by the receiver.

Cryptography or communication protocols are essential for the transmission of sensitive data. These methods are widely used to protect e-mail messages, credit card information, and corporate data.

The following situation was reported by the Associated Press:

AP June 12, 2007

> The personal health information of more than 9,000 Concord Hospital patients was exposed on the Internet for more than a month. The hospital's president said there's no way of knowing whether any were poached by criminals.
>
> The hospital sent letters last week notifying 9,297 patients and confirmed the breach Saturday to local media. A statement posted Sunday on its website said Concord Hospital was working to ensure no future security lapses.
>
> Concord Hospital said Verus, Inc., its online billing contractor, disabled an electronic firewall protecting the information on April 12 to perform maintenance, then inadvertently left if off. Verus notified Concord Hospital of the breach on May 30.

1. In this situation, who is responsible for the security breach?
2. What risks do the patients face, in your opinion?
3. What steps is Concord Hospital likely to require its business associate, Verus, Inc., to take in the future to protect the security of Concord's ePHI?

Antivirus Software

Antivirus software scans a system for known viruses. After detection, the antivirus software attempts to remove the virus from the system and, in some cases, fix any problems the virus created. Antivirus tools cannot detect and eliminate all viruses. New viruses are continually being developed, and antivirus software must be regularly updated to maintain its effectiveness.

> **COMPLIANCE TIP**
>
> **Internet Security Symbol**
>
> On the Internet, when an item is secure, a small padlock appears in the status bar at the bottom of the browser window.
>
> The padlock symbol shows that encryption is being used.

Organization of the HIPAA Security Standards

The HIPAA Security Rule contains specific standards that give direction on how to meet its requirements. The standards are organized into three categories, as shown in Figure 3-3.

Figure 3-3

The HIPAA Security Standards Categories

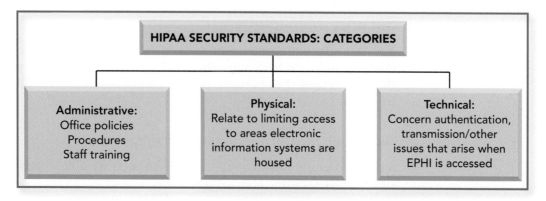

HIPAA SECURITY STANDARDS: CATEGORIES

Administrative:	Physical:	Technical:
Office policies Procedures Staff training	Relate to limiting access to areas electronic information systems are housed	Concern authentication, transmission/other issues that arise when EPHI is accessed

ADMINISTRATIVE, PHYSICAL, AND TECHNICAL STANDARDS

Administrative standards relate to the administrative actions that a covered entity must perform, or train staff to do, to carry out security requirements. These actions include implementing office policies and procedures for ways to prevent, detect, contain, and correct security violations. **Physical standards** require covered entities to implement policies and procedures that limit unauthorized physical access to electronic information systems such as computers as well as the facilities where the ePHI is stored. **Technical standards** require CEs to create policies and procedures that govern the technical aspects of accessing ePHI within computer systems by appropriate personnel.

IMPLEMENTATION SPECIFICATIONS

Along with each category of HIPAA security standards are **implementation specifications** that provide specific details on how to implement them. There are two types of implementation specifications, those that are required and those that must be addressed. **Required implementation specifications** must be in place just as described by the standard. **Addressable implementation specifications** are guidelines that must be "addressed" (covered); the CE must in some manner accomplish the goal of the specifications or document why it did not do so.

COMPLIANCE TIP

Required Records

For all standards and implementation specifications, CEs must maintain a current document that explains their compliance process. This document must be retained for six years from either the date it was created or the date it last went into effect, whichever is later, and remain available to those persons responsible for implementing the procedures.

Administrative Standards

According to the HIPAA Security Rule, the administrative standards guide actions, policies, and procedures that manage the security measures to protect ePHI and also manage the conduct of the covered entity's workforce in relation to the protection of that information. The provisions and implementation specifications are shown in Table 3-2, and the major concepts are explained below.

KEY PROVISIONS

The HIPAA administrative standards include nine key points, each guiding a particular aspect of security.

Security Management Process

The security management process requires the CE to perform a risk analysis and then to manage the risk by having policies and procedures that are designed to prevent, detect, contain, and correct HIPAA security violations.

Assigned Security Responsibility

A covered entity has to appoint a HIPAA security officer who is responsible for its security policies and procedures.

TABLE 3-2	Administrative Safeguards	
STANDARDS	**IMPLEMENTATION SPECIFICATIONS** **(R) = REQUIRED, (A) = ADDRESSABLE**	
Security Management Process	Risk analysis	(R)
	Risk management	(R)
	Sanction policy	(R)
	Information system activity review	(R)
Assigned Security Responsibility		
Workforce Security	Authorization and/or supervision	(A)
	Workforce clearance procedure	(A)
	Termination procedures	(A)
Information Access Management	Isolating health care	(R)
	Clearinghouse functions	
	Access authorization	(A)
	Access establishment and modification	(A)
Security Awareness and Training	Security reminders	(A)
	Protection from malicious software	(A)
	Log-in monitoring	(A)
	Password management	(A)
Security Incident Procedures	Response and reporting	(R)
Contingency Plan	Data backup plan	(R)
	Disaster recovery plan	(R)
	Emergency mode operation plan	(R)
	Testing and revision procedures	(A)
	Applications and data criticality analysis	(A)
Evaluation		
Business Associate Contracts and Other Arrangements	Written contract or other arrangement	(R)

Workforce Security

The workforce security standard requires a CE to have policies and procedures in place to ensure that all employees who should have access to ePHI do have access. For each workforce member, or job function, the covered entity must identify the ePHI that is needed and when it is needed, and make reasonable efforts to control access to it. This also includes identification of the computer systems and applications that provide access to the ePHI. Covered entities must provide only the minimum necessary access to ePHI that is required for a workforce member to do his or her job. Policies must also ensure that employees who should *not* access ePHI are unable to do so.

COMPLIANCE TIP

Security Officer

For a small CE, such as a small physician practice, the HIPAA security officer is often the same individual as the HIPAA privacy official. In large facilities, the security officer might be the director of the information technology or health information management department.

Information Access Management

A CE has to have procedures for authorizing employees' access to ePHI. In HIPAA security terms, **authorization** is the process of determining whether a particular user (or a computer system) has the right to carry out a certain activity, such as reading a file or running a program.

Security Awareness and Training

A CE must train its employees about the security policies and procedures. (Initial security training was required by the compliance date of the rule.) Periodic retraining should be given whenever environmental or operational changes affect the security of ePHI. Changes may include new or updated policies and procedures, new or upgraded software or hardware, new security technology, or changes that are announced in the Security Rule itself.

Security Incident Procedures

A CE also must have policies and procedures in place to address **security incidents,** defined in the law as "the attempted or successful unauthorized access, use, disclosure, modification, or destruction of information or interference with system operations in an information system." The CE's security documents must explain how to identify security incidents and to whom they should be reported.

Contingency Plan

A CE must set up policies and procedures for responding to an emergency or other occurrences that threaten the security of electronic records, such as a power outage, fire, natural disaster, or computer system failure. The goal is to ensure that CEs have ePHI available when it is needed.

Evaluation

Ongoing evaluation of a CE's policies and procedures should be conducted to update the risk analysis and handle changing situations.

Business Associate Contracts

Covered entities must have wording in their contracts with business associates (see Chapter 1) that require them to comply with the HIPAA security standards.

IMPLEMENTATION SPECIFICATIONS FOR ADMINISTRATIVE STANDARDS

A number of implementation specifications are part of the administrative standards; the following are key points.

Sanction Policy

A key specification is the required **sanction policy** that CEs must have. It should state the consequences for violations of security policies and procedures by employees, agents, and contractors. Violations could result in actions ranging from retraining the employee who violated the policies and procedures to terminating the individual if the violation is egregious. Sanctions must be applied equally to all individuals, and the policy should apply to any and all violations.

Workforce Clearance Procedures

An important addressable implementation specification is the need to have workforce clearance procedures, which ensure that individuals who have access to ePHI have been given appropriate clearance, such as a background check before being hired.

Data Backup Plan

Most CEs have data **backup procedures** as part of normal business activities, and this is a required implementation specification under the administrative standards. Backing up is the activity of copying files to another medium (such as tape, disk, CD, or online backup service) so that they will be preserved in case the originals are no longer available. A successful backup plan is critical in recovering from either a minor or major security incident that jeopardizes critical data. For the health care industry, a backup plan must review all the important sources of data, such as:

> Patient accounting systems

> Electronic medical (health) records

> Health maintenance and case management information

> Digital files of diagnostic images and test results

Disaster Recovery Plan

Disaster recovery has taken on new urgency in recent years. As CEs' reliance on computers has increased, so have the threats of terrorism, hackers, and computer viruses. A disaster recovery plan, as required under the administrative standards, details activities and preparations to minimize loss and ensure continuity of critical business functions in the event of a major disaster. The types of events addressed by a disaster recovery plan typically include:

> Natural disasters (earthquake, fire, flood, storm)

> Terrorist acts (explosion, chemical weapons, hostage-taking)

> Power disruptions and power failures

> Computer software or hardware failures

> Computer shutdowns (effects of hacker, virus)

> Labor problems (strike, slowdown, walkout)

Emergency Mode Operation Plan

To ensure availability in emergency situations, one of the three goals of the security standards, CEs must implement an emergency mode operation plan.

Physical Standards

Physical security means the protection of building sites and equipment from theft, vandalism, natural disasters, and accidental damage. It includes controlling the environment in which the electronic systems operate and handling electrical power (noise, brownout, humidity, and static), fire detection and suppression, heating, ventilation, and air conditioning. Physical security also includes ways to control access such as locks, guards, surveillance monitors, intrusion detectors, and alarms. It includes maintaining appropriate controls of files that are retained, stored, or scheduled for destruction. The physical safeguards and implementation specifications are presented in Table 3-3; major provisions are explained below.

KEY PROVISIONS

The HIPAA physical standards are as follows:

> *Facility access controls:* Mechanisms must be in place to ensure that only authorized staff members can enter the premises and remove systems or media containing ePHI. An example of a mechanism is a log for a physician practice that identifies all employees who have security codes for entering the facility and also for locking up the premises at the end of the work day.

> *Workstation use:* A **workstation** is an electronic computing device such as a laptop or desktop computer and electronic media stored in its immediate area. CEs must have policies and procedures that describe appropriate functions for a specific workstation or classes of workstations that are used to access ePHI. An example of this

TABLE 3-3	Physical Safeguards	
STANDARDS	**IMPLEMENTATION SPECIFICATIONS** **(R) = REQUIRED, (A) = ADDRESSABLE**	
Facility Access Controls	Contingency	(A)
	Facility security plan	(A)
	Access control and validation procedures	(A)
	Maintenance records	(A)
Workstation Use		
Workstation Security		
Device and Media Controls	Disposal	(R)
	Media reuse	(R)
	Accountability	(A)
	Data backup and storage	(A)

standard is restricting the ePHI available on a reception area computer to only the ePHI needed to schedule or change appointments.

> *Workstation security:* Mechanisms must be in place to ensure that computer workstations and all other devices are secure and are used appropriately. For example, physically attaching a computer to a desk so that it cannot be removed by a thief meets this standard.

> *Device and media controls:* A CE must have policies and procedures that ensure security when moving computers and/or other electronic media (for example, backup tapes and flash drives) that contain ePHI within and outside the facility. An example of a policy that meets is this standard is to remove all sensitive information from the computer before transferring it to another user.

IMPLEMENTATION SPECIFICATIONS FOR PHYSICAL STANDARDS

Two implementation specifications are required for the HIPAA physical standards. The disposal implementation specification requires CEs to address the final disposition of ePHI. When disposed of, the media must be made unusable or inaccessible. Simply deleting files or formatting drives is not sufficient. One effective method of disposal is **degaussing,** in which a strong magnetic field is applied to fully erase the data. Another method is to physically break, burn, or destroy the media beyond repair.

CEs may reuse media instead of destroying it. In this case, the media reuse implementation specification requires a CE to ensure that all storage media containing ePHI (such as CDs and DVDs) are carefully cleansed of all data and images before being reused. This cleansing is usually done by running a software program designed to completely remove the data.

COMPLIANCE TIP

Retention

According to the American Health Information Management Association (AHIMA), record retention requirements are at least ten years for transactional/billing records and for law enforcement purposes. Medical histories should be retained indefinitely.

Which physical standard is addressed in each of the following examples?

1. The screens on computers are turned so they cannot be seen by casual observers.
2. The computer is located in a locked office and can be accessed by authorized employees only.
3. The medical biller who works from her home is required to follow the CE's policies regarding ePHI.
4. The hospital policy is to degauss all storage media.

HIPAA ⚠ **CAUTION**

E-Discovery

Under rule changes effective December 1, 2006, from the Federal Rules of Civil Procedure, organizations may be required to provide electronic documents in civil law cases. **E-discovery,** the process of gathering information from digital sources, is a growing part of legal proceedings, and covered entities' retention policies will be altered in the future to meet the new requirements.

Technical Standards

The technical safeguards are defined as "the technology and the policy and procedures for its use that protect ePHI and control access to it." Many different technology solutions are available for security, and the HIPAA security standards do not specify particular choices. Technical safeguards and implementation specifications are presented in Table 3-4, and key points are explained below.

KEY PROVISIONS

The key provisions of the technical (technology) safeguards include:

> *Access controls:* In the HIPAA security standards, access means the ability to read, write, modify, or communicate data and information. CEs must have policies and procedures to ensure appropriate

TABLE 3-4	Technical Safeguards	
STANDARDS	**IMPLEMENTATION SPECIFICATIONS** **(R) = REQUIRED, (A) = ADDRESSABLE**	
Access Control	Unique user	(R)
	Emergency access procedure	(R)
	Automatic logoff	(A)
	Encryption and decryption	(A)
Audit Controls		
Integrity	Mechanism to authenticate electronic protected health information	(A)
Person or Entity Authentication		
Transmission Security	Integrity controls	(A)
	Encryption	(A)

access to ePHI by authorized individuals only. Passwords are required for authorized individuals.

> *Audit controls:* CEs must use hardware, software, and/or procedural mechanisms that monitor ePHI for security breaches.

> *Integrity:* CEs must protect ePHI from improper alteration or destruction.

> *Person or entity authentication:* **Authentication** is the process of ensuring that a person is in fact who he or she claims to be before allowing the person to access ePHI. CEs must implement procedures to verify that a person or entity seeking access to ePHI is the one claimed. A covered entity may handle authentication in one of three ways:

> Require the person to enter something known only to that individual, such as a password.

> Require something a person possesses, such as a smart card, token, or key.

> Require something unique to the individual, such as a *biometric* like fingerprints, voice patterns, facial patterns, or iris patterns.

Authentication of remote users in Internet or other networks often relies on a technique called a **digital certificate.** This is an electronic authorization that is issued to remote users by a covered entity. Digital certificates are digital files that certify the identity of an individual or institution seeking access to computer-based information. In enabling such access, they serve the same purpose as a driver's license or library card. The digital certificate links the identifier of an individual or institution to a digital *public key.* Digital certificates are part of the Secure Socket Layer (SSL) protocol, which enables secure electronic transactions on the Internet.

> *Transmission security:* CEs must have technical security measures to guard against access to ePHI that is being transmitted over an electronic communications network (for example, using secure transmission systems or encryption when e-mailing or transmitting patient data).

IMPLEMENTATION SPECIFICATIONS FOR TECHNICAL STANDARDS

For this category, there are seven implementation specifications, two of which are required.

Unique User Identification (Required)

A **unique user identification** is a required implementation specification. This means that every individual in the workplace must have his or her own unique name and/or number for access to the computer system. Sharing user identifications is not permitted.

Emergency Access Procedure Required

The technical safeguards also require a procedure to be in place for accessing ePHI if there is an emergency.

COMPLIANCE TIP

Emergency Procedures

Many CEs include the emergency access procedure as part of their general emergency procedures.

Which technology safeguard is represented by each of the following policies?

1. E-mail sent from the provider to the clearinghouse is encrypted.
2. The hospital IT system automatically creates a log that shows who accessed a particular computer and when.
3. Each individual authorized to work with patient records has a unique password.
4. A health plan installs an antivirus program on all its computers and keeps it up to date.
5. Access to the hospital's record storage area requires swiping a hospital-provided smart card.

HIPAA Security Standards: Portable and/or Mobile Media, Faxes, and E-mail

Two activities, using portable media devices and sending fax transmissions and e-mail, can put ePHI at special risk. CEs must understand the special factors that are involved with them.

PORTABLE AND/OR MOBILE MEDIA GUIDANCE

Since the **HIPAA** security standards went into effect, many new technologies have been introduced that have changed the way medical personnel work with ePHI. No longer is it typical to work with patients' medical information in an office setting only. In manysituations, portable equipment that has improved record-keeping efficiency is used:

> A health plan employee takes backup plan subscriber data to an off-site storage facility.

> A physician accesses an e-prescribing program while out of the office and responds to patients' requests for refills.

> A home health nurse collects patient data while visiting patients and enters the information into a laptop computer.

While these technologies provide administrative benefits, security incidents related to their use have increased. The main concern is protecting ePHI when CEs allow remote access to data through portable devices or on external systems or hardware that they do not own or manage. Widely used **portable and/or mobile media devices** include:

> USB flash drives and memory cards

> Laptop computers

> Personal digital assistants (PDAs) and smart phones

> Home computers

> Hotel, library, or other public workstations and wireless access points (WAPs)

> Backup media

> Remote access devices (including security hardware)

Because of the concern by the federal government, the *HIPAA Security Guidance for Remote Use of and Access to Electronic Protected Health Information* has been published. It emphasizes that CEs should be extremely cautious about allowing the off-site use of ePHI.

Security incidents can occur during access, storage, or transmission. Basic guidelines are as follows:

> Strictly limit remote access to ePHI to authorized users based on their roles within the organization and their need for access to ePHI.

> Back up all ePHI entered into remote systems.

> Employ encryption on all portable or remote devices that store PHI.

> Install virus protection software on portable devices.

Special security incident procedures should cover the steps that should be taken if there is loss of ePHI through the use of portable media. Employees may need to save evidence of criminal activities, manage the harmful effects of improper use or disclosure, and notify affected parties. A sanction policy must explain the consequences of failing to comply with the security policies and procedures related to off-site use of, or access to, ePHI.

SENDING FAXES AND E-MAIL

Likewise, if a covered entity sends faxes and e-mail, HIPAA requires taking reasonable steps to protect PHI, as well as limiting the information to the minimum necessary to meet the purpose of the request. There is a danger that the fax or e-mail will be sent to an unauthorized receiver, threatening the confidentiality of the information. The following administrative procedures are recommended:

> Double-check the recipient's fax number or e-mail address before transmittal and confirm delivery via telephone or review of the appropriate confirmation.

> Include a **confidentiality notice** (see Figure 3-4) on all fax cover sheets and on e-mail. The statement should instruct the receiver to destroy the materials and contact the sender immediately in the event that the transmission has reached him or her in error.

Physical safeguards are also recommended:

> Place fax machines in areas that require security keys, badges, or similar mechanisms for access.

> Periodically remind regular fax or e-mail recipients to provide notification in the event that their fax numbers or e-mail addresses change.

INTERNET RESOURCE

HIPAA Security Guidance

www.cms.hhs.gov/ SecurityStandard/ Downloads/Security GuidanceforRemoteUse Final122806.pdf

COMPLIANCE TIP

Employment Prerequiste Possible

HIPAA security guidance states that a covered entity should consider requiring employees to sign a statement of adherence to security policies.

Figure 3-4
Confidentiality Notice for
Faxes and E-mail

CONFIDENTIALITY NOTICE: This transmission, including any attachments to it, may contain confidential information or protected health information subject to privacy regulations such as the Health Insurance Portability and Accountability Act of 1996 (HIPAA). This transmission is intended only for the use of the recipient(s) named above. If you are not the intended recipient or a person responsible for delivering it to the intended recipient, you are hereby notified that any disclosure, copying, distribution, or use of any of the information contained in this transmission is STRICTLY PROHIBITED. If you have received this transmission in error, please immediately notify me by reply e-mail, and destroy the original transmission in its entirety without saving it in any manner.

HIPAA ⚠ CAUTION

Confidentiality Notices

Although they are not required, confidentiality notices provide added legal protection. They do not, however, absolve the sender of liability if the information reaches the wrong party.

A technical security service in the case of faxes involves making certain that audit controls, like fax transmittal summaries and confirmation sheets, are stored and reviewed periodically for unauthorized access or use. Preprogram and test destination numbers in order to minimize the potential for human error.

Case Discussion

At the beginning of the chapter, three cases were presented. These are reviewed below, with discussion of how the HIPAA security standards could have been applied to block the breach.

CASE 1

A medical assistant faxed the results of a patient's TB test to the wrong specialist's office.

Discussion: This wrongful disclosure could have been avoided if the receiver's fax number had been verified before transmission. To mitigate problems, a preprinted confidentiality statement on the fax cover sheet should instruct the receiver to destroy the faxed materials and contact the sender immediately in the event that the transmission reached him or her in error.

CASE 2

The Department of Veterans Affairs announced that all agency computers would be upgraded with data security encryption immediately. The move came in the wake of a second theft of a VA laptop from a vendor's office. Laptops would be the first to receive the encryption programs, followed by desktop computers and portable media.

Discussion: From an administrative viewpoint, the physical security of laptops at all sites should be secured, and the vendor, as a business associate of the agency, should have its physical safety guidelines in place. Encrypting data on laptops and other computers will effectively halt access to the ePHI.

CASE 3

A thief stole backup tapes from the van of a provider's employee who had taken the tapes in order to do some work over the weekend. The provider waited for more than three weeks to tell the state department of justice and the patients about the loss of personal medical and financial information. The provider was later ordered by the state to provide twelve months of free credit monitoring to patients affected by the data breach. The provider also had to pay patient claims for any losses directly resulting from the data theft.

Discussion: The provider's security incident procedures should provide for quick notification of the unlawful disclosure of electronic protected health information. Likewise, employees should not take patient data home unless specifically authorized to do so.

CHAPTER REVIEW

CHAPTER SUMMARY

1. Electronic protected health information (ePHI) is PHI that is stored or transmitted in electronic form. Electronic storage includes computer systems and storage devices of all types. Electronic transmission methods include Internet, computer networks within organizations, and ePHI that is physically moved from one location to another using magnetic tape, disks, CDs, flash drives, or any other removable medium.

2. The three goals of the HIPAA security standards apply to ePHI. The goals are to ensure its (a) confidentiality, (b) integrity, and (c) availability.

3. The HIPAA security standards require covered entities to analyze and then manage the risk that any ePHI they possess could be accessed by anyone other than appropriate and authorized individuals. Risk analysis means that the CE must examine and document any potential threats to the security of their information. Risk management means establishing policies and procedures that reduce the risk of security breaches.

4. Identity theft occurs when a criminal uses another person's personal information to take on that person's identity for financial gain.

5. The HIPAA Security Rule is organized into three categories: (a) administrative standards, covering office policies and procedures for ways to prevent, detect, contain, and correct security violations; (b) physical standards, requiring policies and procedures that limit unauthorized physical access to electronic information systems such as computers as well as storage facilities; and (c) technical standards, requiring policies and procedures that govern the technical aspects of accessing ePHI within computer systems by appropriate personnel.

6. Implementation specifications are to be used as guidelines for covered entities in following the administrative, physical, and technical standards. Required implementation specifications must be performed as described in the standard, while addressable implementation specifications serve as guidelines that must be considered.

7. The nine administrative safeguards are:

    > *Security management process,* requiring risk analysis and management through policies and procedures that are designed to prevent, detect, contain, and correct HIPAA security violations

> *Assigned security responsibility,* requiring appointment of a HIPAA security officer

> *Workforce security,* requiring policies and procedures to ensure that all employees who should have access to ePHI do have access and that employees who should *not* access ePHI are unable to do so

> *Information access management,* requiring procedures for authorizing employees' access to ePHI

> *Security awareness and training,* requiring employee training about the security policies and procedures

> *Security incident procedures,* requiring policies and procedures to address security incidents

> *Contingency plan,* requiring policies and procedures for responding to an emergency or other occurrences that threaten the security of electronic records

> *Evaluation,* requiring keeping policies and procedures updated

> *Business associate contracts,* requiring BAs to comply with the HIPAA security standards

8. The physical safeguards are:

> *Facility access controls,* requiring mechanisms to ensure that only authorized staff members can enter the premises and remove systems or media containing ePHI

> *Workstation use,* requiring policies and procedures that describe appropriate functions for a specific workstation or class of workstations that are used to access ePHI

> *Workstation security,* requiring policies and procedures to ensure that computer workstations and all other devices are secure and are used appropriately

> *Device and media controls,* requiring policies and procedures that ensure security when moving computers and/or other electronic media that contain ePHI within and outside the facility

9. The technical safeguards are:

> *Access controls,* requiring policies and procedures to ensure only appropriate access to ePHI by authorized individuals

> *Audit controls,* requiring the use of hardware, software, and/or procedural mechanisms that monitor ePHI for security breaches

> *Integrity,* requiring protection of ePHI from improper alteration or destruction

> *Person or entity authentication,* requiring procedures to verify that a person or entity seeking access to ePHI is the one claimed

> *Transmission security,* requiring technical security measures to guard against access to ePHI that is being transmitted over an electronic communications network

10. The HIPAA security considerations for portable and/or mobile devices advise covered entities to be extremely cautious about allowing off-site use of ePHI and, when off-site use does make business sense, to limit access, back up ePHI entered into a remote system, and use encryption and antivirus protection software. Faxes and e-mail are permitted, but the covered entity must take reasonable steps to protect the ePHI and limit the release to the minimum necessary. A confidentiality notice is considered extra protection.

MATCHING QUESTIONS

Match the key terms with their definitions.

__b__ 1. confidentiality

__e__ 2. integrity

__j__ 3. availability

__f__ 4. implementation specifications

__i__ 5. administrative standards

__h__ 6. technical standards

__g__ 7. physical standards

__c__ 8. malware

__a__ 9. authentication

__d__ 10. role-based authorization

a. Process of ensuring that a person is in fact who he or she claims to be before allowing the person to access ePHI.

b. Ensuring that the information is shared only among authorized individuals or organizations.

c. Program that harms information systems.

d. Allowing access according to job title and/or function.

e. Making sure the information is not changed in any way during storage or transmission.

f. Required and addressable guidelines for implementing various HIPAA security standards.

g. Policies and procedures that limit unauthorized physical access to electronic information systems.

h. Policies and procedures that govern the technical aspects of accessing ePHI within computer systems by appropriate personnel.

    i. Office policies and procedures for ways to prevent, detect, contain, and correct security violations.

    j. Ensuring that the systems responsible for delivering, storing, and processing data are accessible, when needed, by those who need them under both routine and emergency circumstances.

TRUE/FALSE QUESTIONS

Decide whether each statement is true or false.

_f_ **1.** The category of ePHI includes all protected health information, including digital and paper records.

_t_ **2.** The three goals of the HIPAA security standards are the confidentiality, integrity, and availability of ePHI.

_f_ **3.** Risk analysis is the process of creating policies and procedures to protect ePHI.

_f_ **4.** The HIPAA Security Rule has four parts: administrative, personnel, technical, and physical.

_t_ **5.** Identity theft can result in loss of money.

_t_ **6.** Required implementation standards must be put into place by covered entities.

_f_ **7.** Passwords can be safely shared with coworkers.

_f_ **8.** Protecting a building from theft, vandalism, natural disasters, and accidental damage is covered under the administrative safeguards.

_f_ **9.** The reuse of storage media is prohibited under HIPAA.

_t_ **10.** Laptop computers are considered portable and/or mobile media devices.

MULTIPLE CHOICE QUESTIONS

Select the letter that best completes the statement or answers the question.

1. What is included in electronic protected health information under HIPAA?

a. digital files

b. printed test results

c. forms completed by patients and filed in storage cabinets

d. all of the above

2. Examples of malware include

a. viruses

b. Trojan horses

c. worms

d. all of the above

3. Appointing a security official for a newly opened clinic is an example of satisfying

a. an administrative security standard

b. a technical security standard

c. a physical security standard

d. an implementation specification

4. Requiring employees to enter a password to authenticate their access to ePHI is an example of satisfying

a. an administrative security standard

b. a technical security standard

c. a physical security standard

d. both an administrative and a technical standard

5. Locking the premises is an example of satisfying

a. an administrative security standard

b. a technical security standard

c. a physical security standard

d. an implementation specification

6. Having backup procedures is an example of satisfying

a. an administrative security standard

b. a technical security standard

c. a physical security standard

d. an implementation specification

7. Security incidents include

a. attempted unauthorized use of ePHI

b. successful unauthorized use of ePHI

c. neither A nor B

d. both A and B

8. A sanction policy

a. establishes the dates of HIPAA compliance

b. states the consequences of violations of security policies and procedures

c. defines physical access procedures

d. sets up rewards for excellence on the part of employees and business associates

9. Cryptography is

a. used to scan computer systems for known viruses

b. used to prevent unauthorized users from gaining access to ePHI

c. protecting information by transforming it into an unreadable format before it is shared

d. role-based authorization

10. A firewall

a. examines traffic entering and leaving a network

b. protects information by transforming it into an unreadable format before it is shared

c. scans computer systems for known viruses

d. contributes to identity theft

SHORT ANSWER QUESTIONS

Answer the following questions.

1. List the three goals for ePHI under the HIPAA Security Rule.

a. _____ Confidentiality _____

b. _____ integrity _____

c. _____ availability _____

2. List the three categories of the HIPAA security standards.

a. _____ administrative _____

b. _____ physical _____

c. _____ technical _____

APPLYING YOUR KNOWLEDGE

HIPAA Cases

1. In each of these cases of release of PHI, was the HIPAA Security Rule followed?

a. A laboratory faxes a patient's medical test results to a physician after verifying the fax number and including a confidentiality notice on the fax cover sheet.

b. A physician serves as the security officer for her solo practice.

c. Because of a flood in the office, all records are destroyed.

d. A hospital requires its personnel to wear ID badges; visitors must sign in at the front desk.

e. A business associate turns off its antivirus program while upgrading its computer system and forgets to turn it on again, with the result that a worm enters its computers and destroys thousands of medical billing records.

f. An employee notices that someone has been tampering with her computer, but she does not report the incident.

g. A hospital uses an encrypted system to e-mail an organ donor's medical information to another hospital that is treating the organ recipient.

h. All the hospital's complete patient medical records for the last ten years are accessible to the medical insurance specialist.

HIPAA Communications

1. ABC Hospital has the Policy #9 document in its Policy and Procedures manual. Study the document below and answer these questions.

   a. What is the purpose of the policy regarding HIPAA security standards?

   b. Name two documents that employees must sign.

   c. What verification checks *could* be made before a person is hired by ABC Hospital? Are other verification checks possible?

   d. Which hospital personnel are responsible for identifying the security responsibilities and supervision for the position?

   e. Does this policy mention sanctions?

WORKFORCE CLEARANCE PROCEDURE

ADMINISTRATIVE MANUAL POLICY #9

HIPAA Security Rule Language: "Implement procedures to determine that the access of a workforce member to ePHI is appropriate."

Policy Summary

The background of all ABC Hospital workforce members must be adequately reviewed during the hiring process. When defining an organizational position, the ABC Hospital human resources department and the hiring manager must identify and define both the security responsibilities of and level of supervision required for the position. All ABC Hospital workforce members who access ABC Hospital information systems containing ePHI must sign a confidentiality agreement. All ABC Hospital employees must also sign a "conditions of employment" document that states their commitment to and understanding of their responsibility for the protection of the confidentiality, integrity, and availability of ABC Hospital's ePHI.

Purpose

This policy reflects ABC Hospital's commitment to ensure that all workforce members have appropriate authorization to access ABC Hospital information systems containing ePHI.

Policy

1. The background of all ABC Hospital workforce members must be adequately reviewed during the hiring process. Verification checks must be made, as appropriate. Verification checks include, but are not limited to:

   - Character references

   - Confirmation of claimed academic and professional qualifications

   - Professional license validation

   - Credit check

   - Criminal background check

   - Office of the Inspector General (OIG) database check

2. The type and number of verification checks conducted must be based on the employee's probable access to ABC Hospital information systems containing ePHI and their expected ability to modify or change such ePHI.

3. The extent and type of screening must be based on ABC Hospital's risk analysis process.

4. When defining a position, the ABC Hospital human resources department manager and the hiring manager must identify the security responsibilities and supervision required for the position. Security responsibilities include general responsibilities for implementing or maintaining security, as well as any specific responsibilities for the protection of the confidentiality, integrity, or availability of ABC Hospital information systems or processes.

5. When job candidates are provided via an agency, ABC Hospital's contract with the agency must clearly state the agency's responsibilities for reviewing the candidates' backgrounds.

6. It is the responsibility of each ABC Hospital department that retains the services of a third party to ensure that the party or person(s) adheres to all appropriate ABC Hospital policies.

7. All ABC Hospital workforce members who access ABC Hospital information systems containing ePHI must sign a confidentiality agreement in which they agree not to provide ePHI to or to discuss confidential information to which they have access with unauthorized persons. Confidentiality agreements must be reviewed and signed annually by ABC Hospital workforce members who access ABC Hospital information systems containing ePHI.

8. All ABC Hospital employees must sign a "conditions of employment" document that affirms their responsibility for the protection of the confidentiality, integrity, or availability of ABC Hospital information systems and processes. The document must include the sanctions that may be applied if employees do not meet their responsibilities.

Scope/Applicability: This policy is applicable to all departments that use or disclose electronic protected health information for any purposes. This policy's scope includes all electronic protected health information.

2. The question and response below have been circulated in an e-mail message to personnel who need to have this information. In your own words, summarize the meaning of the answer, addressing these points:

a. Is encryption mandatory under the HIPAA Security Rule? Why?

b. What kind of guidance is under discussion?

QUESTION

Is mandatory encryption in the HIPAA Security Rule?

RESPONSE

No. The final HIPAA Security Rule made the use of encryption an addressable implementation specification. See 45 CFR §§ 164.312(a)(2)(iv) and 164.312(e)(2)(ii). Covered entities use open networks such as the Internet and e-mail systems differently, and no single interoperable encryption solution for communicating over open networks exists. Setting a single encryption standard could have placed an unfair financial and technical burden on some covered entities. The encryption implementation specification is addressable, and must therefore be implemented if, after an assessment, the entity has determined that the specification is a reasonable and appropriate safeguard in its environment. If the entity decides that the addressable implementation specification is not reasonable and appropriate, it must document that determination and implement an equivalent alternative measure, presuming that the alternative is reasonable and appropriate, or if the standard can otherwise be met, the covered entity may choose to not implement the implementation specification or any equivalent alternative measure.

RESEARCHING THE INTERNET

1. Using a web browser such as Google or Yahoo, search for and report on current information about the Federal Identity Theft Task Force. Specifically review suggestions for improved authentication procedures.

2. The National Institute for Standards and Technology (NIST) offers advice on security log management. Visit the NIST home page and locate the Computer Security Division (CSD) of NIST's Information Technology Laboratory. What is stated as the CSD's mission statement?

The HIPAA Transactions, Code Sets, and National Identifier Standards

4

CHAPTER OUTLINE

LEARNING OUTCOMES

After studying this chapter, you should be able to:

1. State the purpose of the HIPAA Electronic Health Care Transactions and Code Sets standards and of the national identifiers.
2. Name eight HIPAA transactions.
3. Identify the key purpose of the Administrative Simplification Compliance Act.
4. List the HIPAA standards for medical code sets.
5. Compare and contrast the ICD-9-CM diagnosis codes, CPT and HCPCS procedure and supply codes, and ICD-9-CM Volume 3 procedure codes.

6. Describe the sources for up-to-date information on changes to the HIPAA medical code sets for diagnoses and procedures.
7. Discuss the general purpose of the HIPAA-mandated administrative code sets.
8. Describe the sources for up-to-date information on changes to the HIPAA administrative code sets.
9. Describe the HIPAA Employer Identifier standard.
10. Describe the HIPAA National Provider Identifier standard.

KEY TERMS

administrative code sets

Administrative Simplification Compliance Act (ASCA)

ASC X12

claim adjustment reason codes (RC)

claim attachment

claim status category codes

claim status codes

code set

Current Dental Terminology (CDT)

Current Procedural Terminology (CPT)

Designated Standard Maintenance Organization (DSMO)

820 Health Plan Premium Payments

834 Health Plan Enrollment and Disenrollment

835 Health Care Payment and Remittance Advice

837 Health Care Claims or Equivalent Encounter Information/Coordination of Benefits

EIN (Employer Identification Number)

Health Care Common Procedure Coding System (HCPCS)

HIPAA Electronic Health Care Transactions and Code Sets (TCS)

HIPAA Employer Identifier

ICD-10-CM

implementation guide

International Classification of Diseases, Ninth Revision, Clinical Modification (ICD-9-CM)

legacy numbers

medical code sets

National Plan and Provider Enumeration System (NPPES)

National Provider Identifier (NPI)

997 Functional Acknowledgment

place of service (POS) code

remittance advice (RA)

remittance advice remark codes (REM)

taxonomy codes

270/271 Eligibility for a Health Plan Inquiry/Response

276/277 Health Care Claim Status Inquiry/Response

278 Referral Certification and Authorization

>> **Why This Chapter Is Important**

This chapter is about the electronic data interchange (EDI) requirements that HIPAA has defined. While necessarily more abstract than privacy or security issues, these requirements are the backbone of achieving the administrative simplification goals of the law. When they are fully implemented in the health care industry, exchange of information will be faster, more efficient, and more accurate.

Allied health personnel work with electronic transactions such as health care claims and insurance verification in many positions. They also work with the diagnosis and procedure codes that are used to communicate the reasons for patient services and also are studied to improve health care. For these reasons, a core understanding of the transactions, code sets, and national identifiers requirements is essential.

HIPAA has established many standards for the particular formats to be used for EDI and for particular lists of codes that numerically represent diagnoses and procedures. HIPAA has also assigned a unique number to each provider in the United States, including individual physicians and organizations such as hospitals and group practices. The new numbers are in effect nationally and replace numbers that had been assigned by various payers in the past. However, although it is mandated by HIPAA, a national system for uniquely identifying a patient moving through the heath care system has not yet been established. In your opinion, what are the pros and cons of using an existing unique number, such as a person's Social Security number, as the HIPAA national identifier for patients?

HIPAA Electronic Health Care Transactions, Code Sets, and National Identifiers

To increase the efficiency of the business of health care, the Administrative Simplification provisions of HIPAA require national standards for electronic health care transactions and national identifiers for covered entities (see Chapter 1). HIPAA requires every provider who does business electronically to use the same health care transactions, code sets, and identifiers for the transmission of health care data. Claims and encounter information, payment and remittance advice, and claim status and inquiry are examples of electronic transactions. The **HIPAA Electronic Health Care Transactions and Code Sets (TCS)** standards (see Figure 4-1 on page 92) have been adopted to make it possible for providers and health plans to exchange these electronic data using standard formats and standard code sets. Covered entities had to comply with the standards by October 23, 2003. Likewise, the HIPAA Employer Identifier and the National Provider Identifier standards mandate using certain identifying numbers for employers that sponsor health plans and for providers.

STANDARD TRANSACTIONS

Transactions, as noted in Chapter 1, are activities involving the transfer of electronic protected health information for specific business purposes. Under HIPAA, if a covered entity sends any one of the HIPAA transactions in an electronic mode, it must comply with the standard for that transaction in all cases. The method of transmission may be over the Internet, via an extranet (using Internet technology to link a business with information accessible to the connected parties only), on leased lines or dial-up lines, and in private networks, or transmissions may be physically moved from a location by transporting storage media.

STANDARD CODE SETS

Under HIPAA, a **code set** is any group of codes used for encoding data elements. **Medical code sets** are used to translate specific diagnosis and clinical procedures into consistent alphanumeric codes. Medical

Figure 4-1

Home Page for Transactions
and Code Sets Regulations

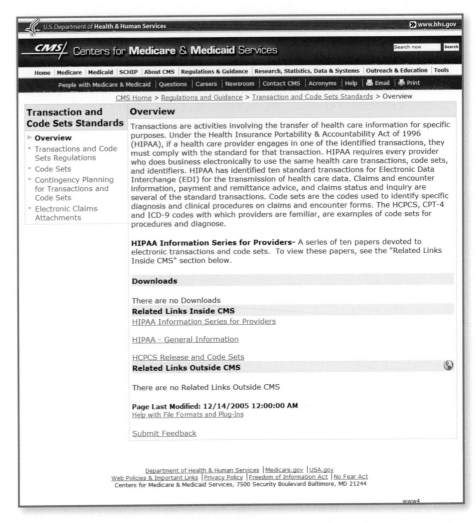

code sets used in the health care industry include coding systems for diseases; treatments and procedures; and supplies or other items used to perform these actions. **Administrative code sets,** or nonmedical code sets, are used to capture general administrative information and range from simple codes, like state abbreviations, to complex codes that give reasons that claims are not being paid.

NATIONAL IDENTIFIERS

Identifiers are numbers of predetermined length and structure, such as a person's Social Security number. They are important because the unique numbers can be used in electronic transactions. HIPAA mandated the development of national identifiers for employers, health care providers, health plans, and patients. These numbers can replace the many numbers that are currently used. Two identifiers have been set up, one for employers and one for providers, and two others are to be established in the future.

Transaction Standards

The HIPAA transaction standards apply to the electronic data that are regularly sent back and forth between providers, health plans, employers, and clearinghouses. Each step in the business process involved with patients who have medical insurance requires certain information to be shared, as shown in Figure 4-2.

EIGHT HIPAA TRANSACTIONS

There are eight mandated HIPAA transactions. The first two HIPAA transactions flow between a health plan and an employer (the plan sponsor):

1. *Health plan premium payments:* Monetary payments of medical insurance premiums for employees enrolled in the health plan sent by employers to payers.

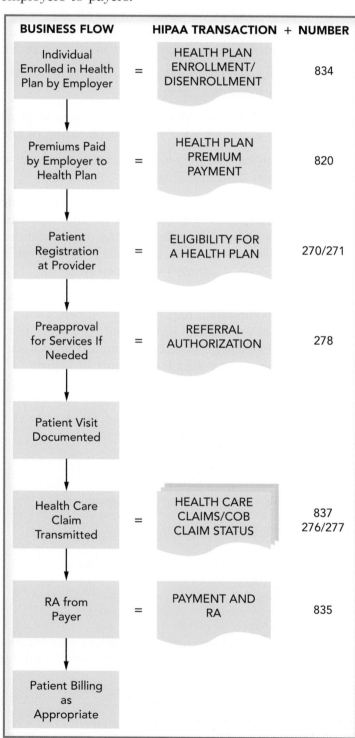

Figure 4-2

Business Flow and HIPAA Transactions

2. *Enrollment or disenrollment in a health plan:* Information about current subscriber status in the health plan.

Then, the following transactions occur as the patient sees the provider, a claim is filed with the health plan (payer), and the payer sends a payment:

3. *Eligibility:* Inquiries sent by providers to payers about a patient's medical insurance benefits to determine whether the payer will cover the planned service or whether, under the terms of the insurance contract, the patient will be responsible for the provider's charges.

4. *Referral certification and authorization:* In health plans that require patients to preapprove visits to specialists, requests a provider makes of a payer for approval to send the patient to another provider.

5. *Claims:* Information sent by providers to payers on behalf of patients who hold medical insurance coverage.

6. *Payment with an explanation:* Money paid by payers to providers in response to claims along with the payer's explanation of benefits.

7. *Claim status:* Inquiries sent by providers to payers about where in the payment process certain claims are.

8. *Coordination of benefits*: Medical insurance policies include explanations of how the policy will pay if more than one insurance policy applies to a claim. This situation can occur when a patient has coverage under two or more plans, such as through employment and also through a spouse's employment.

A ninth standard covering **claim attachments,** supplemental health information needed to support a particular health care claim, is pending approval. Examples are clinical reports and laboratory test results. Finally, HIPAA requires passage of a tenth standard for a document in workers' compensation cases called First Report of Injury.

FYI

The term *X12* also often appears with the name of a transaction because the American National Standards Institute (ANSI) accredits committees as Accredited Standards Committees (ASC), and **ASC X12** is the U.S. standards body for the cross-industry development, maintenance, and publication of electronic data exchange standards such as the X12 EDI format.

HIPAA ⚠ CAUTION

Paper Claims and other Nonelectronic Transactions

HIPAA standards apply only to electronic transactions conducted by covered entities (CEs). Health plans (payers) may require paper claims to have the same data elements, codes, and identifiers as HIPAA claims.

COMPLIANCE TIP

Two Numbers in Transaction Names

If the transaction has two numbers, the first is from the provider to the plan, and the second is from the plan back to the provider.

NUMBER	OFFICIAL NAME
820	Health Plan Premium Payments
834	Health Plan Enrollment and Disenrollment
270/271	Eligibility for a Health Plan Inquiry/Response
278	Referral Certification and Authorization
837	Health Care Claims or Equivalent Encounter Information/Coordination of Benefits
275	*Additional Information to Support a Health Care Claim or Encounter (Claim Attachment; pending approval)*
276/277	Health Care Claim Status Inquiry/Response
835	Health Care Payment and Remittance Advice

In the HIPAA EDI rules, each standard has both a number and a name. Either the number (such as "the 837") or the name (such as the "HIPAA claim") may be used in the industry to refer to the particular electronic document format.

WHAT DO THE TRANSACTIONS COVER?

Each HIPAA transaction covers a typical function in the business flow of medical insurance.

834 Health Plan Enrollment and Disenrollment

The **834 Health Plan Enrollment and Disenrollment** transaction standard covers activities to determine whether a patient is a member of a health plan and eligible for health benefits (enrollment) or is no longer eligible for benefits (disenrollment).

820 Health Plan Premium Payments

The **820 Health Plan Premium Payments** transaction standard gives the receiver of the premium payment (the insurance company) information to properly apply the payment to an individual's account.

270/271 Eligibility for a Health Plan Inquiry/Response

The **270/271 Eligibility for a Health Plan Inquiry/Response** provides health care providers with a way to determine whether the patient is covered for a specific service. The answer helps the provider decide what the billing process will be for the patient. If not covered, the patient is responsible for the charges. If covered, the provider will usually file a claim with the payer on the patient's behalf, and the patient will owe the balance after the insurance pays.

278 Referral Certification and Authorization

The **278 Referral Certification and Authorization** transaction standard is used by providers to find out whether particular services require preauthorization in order to be covered by the health plan. If they do, the health plan transmits a referral number that is entered on the claim when transmitted for payment.

837 Health Care Claims or Equivalent Encounter Information/Coordination of Benefits

The **837 Health Care Claims or Equivalent Encounter Information/Coordination of Benefits** transaction is the health care claim sent from providers to health plans (payers). Hospitals send a transaction called the 827 Institutional, and physicians send the 837 Professional. The first claim sent is the health care claim. If the patient has an additional insurance coverage, then, after the first claim is paid, another claim (the coordination of benefits claim) is sent to the secondary insurance plan.

276/277 Health Care Claim Status Inquiry/Response

The **276 Health Care Claim Status Inquiry** is sent by a provider to a health plan to find out where in the claim adjudication process a particular claim is. The **277 Health Care Claim Status Response** is the reply from the health plan. If the health plan is waiting for information to process the claim, it can send an unsolicited 277 to notify the provider that the claim cannot be paid as submitted.

835 Health Care Payment and Remittance Advice

The **835 Health Care Payment and Remittance Advice** covers two parts of the health plan's payment for a claim. The first part is the payment itself, and the second part is a **remittance advice** (**RA;** also called an *electronic remittance advice* or an *explanation of benefits*), which explains how the payment was arrived at. For example, a health plan may have denied payment for a charge on a bill, but has paid the rest. As covered later in the chapter, the RA contains administrative codes as needed to detail each part of the payment decision.

997 Functional Acknowledgment

Although not a HIPAA standard, the **997 Functional Acknowledgment** transaction is commonly used to acknowledge that a particular message has been sent and received. The 997 is sent from the receivers to the senders of transaction to tell them the transaction has been received without any transmission errors.

Figure 4-3 shows the exchange of information that occurs once a claim is filed by a provider with a payer.

WHO MUST COMPLY?

All covered entities must comply with the general provisions and the regulations on standard code sets. For the transactions, the focus has been on health care claims. If the provider has sent (or has hired a clearinghouse to send) any claim to any health plan electronically, then it has to send all claims electronically. This umbrella covers most providers, since nearly all providers recognize that electronic claims are paid faster and that the electronic payment with the remittance advice that is returned is processed faster.

Administrative Simplification Compliance Act

Because of outdated computer systems and the need to change from old to new information technology, some CEs continued to send paper claims after the HIPAA regulations went into effect. To address this, the **Administrative Simplification Compliance Act (ASCA)** amended the Health Insurance Portability and Accountability Act of 1996 (HIPAA) and required that all claims submitted to Medicare as of October 16, 2003, be sent electronically, except in the following circumstances:

❯ A small provider (fewer than ten full-time employees)

❯ A dentist

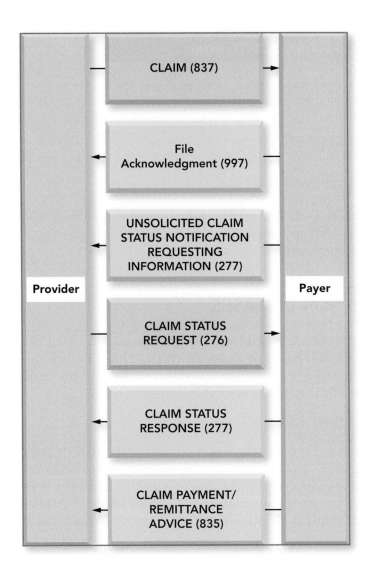

Figure 4-3
General Claim-to-Payment Data Exchange

The figure shows a data exchange between Provider and Payer:

- CLAIM (837)
- File Acknowledgment (997)
- UNSOLICITED CLAIM STATUS NOTIFICATION REQUESTING INFORMATION (277)
- CLAIM STATUS REQUEST (276)
- CLAIM STATUS RESPONSE (277)
- CLAIM PAYMENT/REMITTANCE ADVICE (835)

> A participant in a Medicare demonstration project

> A provider that conducts mass immunizations

> Home oxygen therapy claims (under certain conditions)

> A provider that submits claims when more than one other payer exists

> A provider that furnishes services outside the United States only

> A provider experiencing a disruption in electricity and/or communications

> An "unusual circumstance," which can be established

Since most providers must send some transactions to the Medicare program, once they comply with the ASCA, they are also then mandated to send all their claims electronically.

Implementation Guides

For each mandated HIPAA transaction, there are **implementation guides** that, like the implementation specifications for the HIPAA security standards, provide detailed technical information on implementing the format.

COMPLIANCE TIP
Paper Claims Will Be Denied

Medicare denies paper claims submitted by electronic submitters unless the submitters have valid waivers on file.

INTERNET RESOURCES
HIPAA Implementation Guides

www.wpc-edi.com/

Since property and casualty insurance programs are not included in the definition of health plan under HIPAA, are they required to use the standard transactions?

Medical Code Sets

As shown in Table 4-1, HIPAA mandates the use of six code sets for presenting clinical information in electronic transactions. The HIPAA code sets home page is shown in Figure 4-4.

ICD-9-CM (VOLUMES 1 AND 2): CODES FOR DISEASES

The diagnosis codes used in the United States are based on the International Classification of Diseases (ICD). The ICD lists diseases and three-digit codes according to a system created and maintained by the World Health Organization of the United Nations.

Background

An American version of the ninth edition of the ICD (ICD-9) was published in 1979. A committee of physicians from various organizations and specialties prepared this version, which is called the ICD-9 Clinical Modification, or the **International Classification of Diseases, Ninth Revision, Clinical Modification,** commonly referred to as **ICD-9-CM.**

TABLE 4-1	HIPAA Standard Code Sets
PURPOSE	**STANDARD CODE SET**
Codes for diseases, injuries, impairments, and other health-related problems	International Classification of Diseases, Ninth Revision, Clinical Modification (ICD-9-CM), Volumes 1 and 2
Codes for procedures or other actions taken to prevent, diagnose, treat, or manage diseases, injuries, and impairments	Physicians' services: Current Procedural Terminology (CPT)
	Inpatient hospital services: International Classification of Diseases, Ninth Revision, Clinical Modification, Volume 3: Procedures
Codes for other medical services	Healthcare Common Procedures Coding System (HCPCS)
Codes for dental services	Current Dental Terminology (CDT-4)
Codes for drugs and biologics from retail pharmacies	National Drug Codes

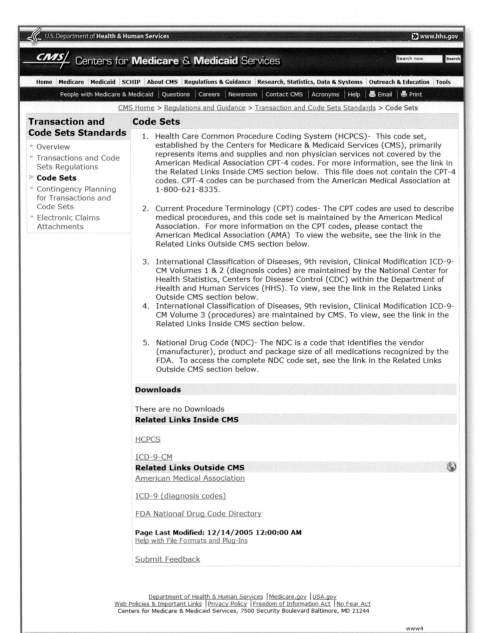

Figure 4-4
Code Sets Home Page

It is used to code and classify morbidity data from patient medical records, physician offices, and surveys conducted by the National Center for Health Statistics.

The Medicare Catastrophic Coverage Act of 1988 mandated the change from written diagnoses to ICD-9-CM diagnosis codes for Medicare claims. After the Medicare ruling, other health plans also began to require providers to report diagnoses with ICD-9-CM codes. Using these diagnosis codes is now law under HIPAA.

An ICD-9-CM diagnosis code has either three, four, or five digits plus a description. The system is built on categories of diseases, injuries, and symptoms. A category has three digits. Most categories have subcategories of four-digit codes. Some codes are further subclassified into five-digit codes.

INTERNET RESOURCE

ICD-9-CM Updates

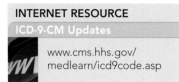

www.cms.hhs.gov/
medlearn/icd9code.asp

COMPLIANCE TIP

Mandated Use of HIPAA
Code Sets

The HIPAA medical code sets used in transactions must be the codes current as of the date of service, not the date the transaction is sent.

Example

Category 415: Acute pulmonary heart disease (three digits)

Subcategory 415.1: Pulmonary embolism and infarction (four digits)

Subclassification: 415.11: Iatrogenic pulmonary embolism and infarction (five digits)

This structure enables coders to assign the most specific diagnosis that is documented in the patient medical record. A fifth digit is more specific than a fourth digit, and a fourth digit is more specific than a three-digit code. When fourth and fifth digits are in ICD-9-CM, they are not optional; they must be used. For example, Centers for Medicare and Medicaid Services (CMS) rules state that a Medicare claim will be rejected when the most specific code available is not used.

ICD-9-CM also has codes for the causes of conditions and for visits where the purpose is health care maintenance rather than a presenting problem.

Staying Up to Date

The National Center for Health Statistics and CMS release ICD-9-CM updates that take effect on October 1 and April 1 of every year. The October 1 changes are the major updates; April 1 is used to catch up on codes that were not included in the major changes. The major new, invalid, and revised codes are posted on the CMS website by the beginning of July for mandated use as of October 1 of that year.

New codes must be used as of the date they go into effect, and invalid (deleted) codes must not be used. The U.S. Government Printing Office (GPO) publishes the official ICD-9-CM on the Internet and in CD-ROM format every year. Various commercial publishers include the updated codes in annual coding books that are printed soon after the July updates are released. Practices must ensure that the current reference is available and that the current codes are in use.

CPT: CODES FOR PHYSICIAN PROCEDURES AND SERVICES

The procedure codes for physicians' and other health care providers' services are selected from the **Current Procedural Terminology** data set, called **CPT,** which is owned and maintained by the American Medical Association (AMA).

Background

CPT was first produced by the American Medical Association in 1966. It began to be widely used in 1983, when the Health Care Financing Administration (now named the Centers for Medicare and Medicaid, or CMS) decided that the CPT codes would be standard for physician procedures paid by Medicare, Medicaid, and other government medical insurance programs.

CPT lists the procedures and services that are commonly performed by physicians across the country. There is also a need for codes for items that are used in medical practices but are not listed in CPT, like supplies and equipment. These codes are found in the Healthcare Common Procedure Coding System (HCPCS). Officially, CPT is the first part (called Level I) of HCPCS, and the supply codes are the second part (Level II). Most people, though, refer to the codes in the CPT book as *CPT codes* and the Level II codes as *HCPCS codes.*

There are three categories of CPT codes:

1. Category I codes
2. Category II codes
3. Category III codes

CPT Category I codes—which are the most numerous—have five digits (with no decimals). Each code has a descriptor, which is a brief explanation of the procedure.

Examples

99204 Office visit for evaluation and management of a new patient

00730 Anesthesia for procedures on upper posterior abdominal wall

24006 Arthrotomy of the elbow, with capsular excision for capsular release

70100 Radiologic examination of the mandible

80400 ACTH stimulation panel; for adrenal insufficiency

93000 Electrocardiogram, routine ECG with at least 12 leads; with interpretation and report

Category II codes are used to track performance measures for a medical goal such as reducing tobacco use. These codes are optional; they are not paid by insurance carriers. They help in the development of best practices for care and improve documentation. These codes have alphabetic characters for the fifth digit.

Examples

0002F Tobacco use, smoking, assessed

0004F Tobacco use cessation intervention, counseling

Category III codes are temporary codes for emerging technology, services, and procedures. These codes also have alphabetic characters for the fifth digit.

Examples

0001T Endovascular repair of infrarenal abdominal aortic aneurysm or dissection

0041T Urinalysis infectious agent detection

A temporary code may become a permanent part of the regular codes if the service it identifies proves effective and is widely performed.

Staying Up to Date

CPT is a proprietary code set, meaning that it is not available for free to the public. Instead, the information must be purchased, either in print or electronic format, from the AMA, which publishes the revised CPT codes. The code books can be purchased in different formats, which range from a basic listing to an enhanced edition.

The annual changes for Category I codes are released by the AMA on October 1 and are in effect for procedures and services provided after January 1 of the following year. The AMA also reports the new codes on its website.

Category II and III codes are prereleased on the AMA website every six months. These codes can be used on their implementation date even before they appear in the printed books.

INTERNET RESOURCE
CPT Updates
www.ama-assn.org/go/CPT

ICD-9-CM (VOLUME 3): CODES FOR HOSPITAL INPATIENT PROCEDURES AND SERVICES

As noted above, ICD-9-CM codes are used for diseases. In fact, the ICD-9-CM has three parts:

1. *Diseases and Injuries: Tabular List—Volume 1:* Seventeen chapters of disease descriptions and codes with two supplementary classifications and five appendixes.

2. *Diseases and Injuries: Alphabetic Index—Volume 2:* (a) An index of the disease descriptions in the Tabular List, (b) an index in table format of drugs and chemicals that cause poisoning, and (c) an index of external causes of injury, such as accidents.

3. *Procedures: Tabular List and Alphabetic Index—Volume 3:* This volume covers procedures performed chiefly in hospitals by physicians and other practitioners.

This third volume, which is maintained by the Centers for Medicare and Medicaid Services, is the HIPAA code set for codes covering hospital inpatient procedures and services. (An inpatient is an individual admitted for at least an overnight stay in a facility such as a hospital.)

Hospital reporting rules require significant procedures to be reported along with the principal diagnosis, comorbidities, and complications. Significant procedures are those that involve surgery, require the use of anesthesia (other than topical), present a risk to the patient, and require specialized training of the physician. The codes contain three to four digits, with two characters placed to the left of the decimal point.

Examples

21.1   Incision of the nose

21.22   Biopsy of the nose

HCPCS: CODES FOR OTHER SUPPLIES AND SERVICES

The **Healthcare Common Procedure Coding System,** referred to as **HCPCS** and pronounced HIC-PIX, was set up to describe specific products, supplies, and services that patients receive that are not in CPT. In the early 1980s, the use of HCPCS codes for claims was optional. With the implementation of HIPAA in 1996, HCPCS has become mandatory.

Description of Codes

A HCPCS code has five characters beginning with a letter followed by four numbers, such as J7630. Each of the more than twenty sections of codes covers a related group of items. For example, the E section covers durable medical equipment (DME), reusable medical equipment ordered by physicians for patients' use at home, such as walkers and wheelchairs.

Staying Up to Date

HCPCS codes are released on January 1 of each year and are reviewed continuously throughout the year. The HCPCS website lists current HCPCS codes, has an alphabetical index of HCPCS codes by type of service or product, and also has an alphabetical table of the drugs for which there are codes.

CDT: CODES FOR DENTAL PROCEDURES

The American Dental Association (ADA) develops and publishes the dental code set, **Current Dental Terminology (CDT).** The five-digit dental procedure codes begin with the letter *D* to differentiate them from numbers in other coding systems. The second number of a CDT code indicates the category of dental service.

Examples

D0120   Periodic Oral Evaluation

D1203   Fluoride—Topical, Child

D2920   Recent Crown

NDC: CODES FOR DRUGS

Under current HIPAA requirements, only retail pharmacies must use the National Drug Codes (NDC) as their code set for drugs and biologicals. Hospitals and physicians are not required to use this code set.

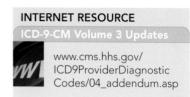

INTERNET RESOURCE

ICD-9-CM Volume 3 Updates

www.cms.hhs.gov/
ICD9ProviderDiagnostic
Codes/04_addendum.asp

COMPLIANCE TIP

HCPCS

CMS is responsible for maintaining the HCPCS code set.

INTERNET RESOURCE

HCPCS Website

www.cms.hhs.gov/
MedHCPCSGenInfo/

1. Each year, ICD-9-CM has many new categories, some for diseases that have been discovered since the previous revision. What are examples of diseases that were first diagnosed in the last two decades?

2. Similarly, many new or improved medical procedures are put into medical practice annually. What are examples of new surgical procedures or tests with which you are familiar?

3. Identify each of the following types of codes.
   A. D2534　　　B. 453.11　　　C. 82000

Administrative Code Sets

HIPAA-mandated administrative code sets support electronic transactions by standardizing codes to present and explain the information that is exchanged. The administrative code sets include various types of codes. Some standards are familiar in everyday use, such as ZIP codes, two-letter state abbreviations, and telephone area codes. Less known but very important are the codes needed to work with the HIPAA transactions effectively:

> Claim status category codes and claim status codes

> Claim adjustment reason codes

> Remittance advice remark codes

> Health care provider taxonomy code set

> Place of service (**POS**) codes

CLAIM STATUS CATEGORY CODES AND CLAIM STATUS CODES

The HIPAA 277 transaction from the payer to the provider uses **claim status category codes** for the main types of responses:

> *A* codes indicate an acknowledgment that the claim has been received.

> *P* codes indicate that a claim is pending; that is, that the payer is waiting for information before making a payment decision.

Figure 4-5

Washington Publishing Company Website

> *F* codes indicate that a claim has been finalized.

> *R* codes indicate that a request for more information has been sent.

> *E* codes indicate that an error has occurred in transmission; usually these claims need to be sent again.

These codes are further detailed in **claim status codes,** as the following examples indicate.

Examples

1 For more detailed information, see remittance advice.

2 More detailed information in letter.

3 Claim has been adjudicated and is awaiting payment cycle.

4 This is a subsequent request for information from the original request.

5 This is a final request for information.

6 Balance due from the subscriber.

7 Claim may be reconsidered at a future date.

9 No payment will be made for this claim.

CLAIM ADJUSTMENT REASON CODES

Payers use **claim adjustment reason codes** (reason codes, abbreviated **RC**) in the 835 transaction (Health Care Payment and Remittance Advice) to provide details about payments that do not match the billed charges. A claim adjustment reason code communicates an adjustment, meaning that it must communicate why a claim or service line was paid differently than it was billed. If there is no adjustment to a claim or line, there is no adjustment reason code.

Examples

1 Deductible amount

2 Coinsurance amount

3 Copayment amount

4 The procedure code is inconsistent with the modifier used, or a required modifier is missing.

5 The procedure code/bill type is inconsistent with the place of service.

6 The procedure/revenue code is inconsistent with the patient's age.

7 The procedure/revenue code is inconsistent with the patient's gender.

8 The procedure code is inconsistent with the provider type/specialty (taxonomy).

9 The diagnosis is inconsistent with the patient's age.

10 The diagnosis is inconsistent with the patient's gender.

INTERNET RESOURCE
Claim Adjustment Reason Codes

www.wpc-edi.com/codes/claimadjustment

REMITTANCE ADVICE REMARK CODES

For even greater detail in the explanation of why payments differ from billed amounts, payers may also use **remittance advice remark codes** (remark codes, **REM**) in the 835 RA transaction. Remark codes are maintained by CMS but can be used by all payers.

Examples

M11 DME, orthotics, and prosthetics must be billed to the DME carrier who services the patient's ZIP code.

M12 Diagnostic tests performed by a physician must indicate whether purchased services are included on the claim.

M37 Service not covered when the patient is under age 35.

M38 The patient is liable for the charges for this service, as you informed the patient in writing before the service was furnished that we would not pay for it, and the patient agreed to pay.

M39 The patient is not liable for payment for this service, as the advance notice of noncoverage you provided the patient did not comply with program requirements.

N14 Payment based on a contractual amount or agreement, fee schedule, or maximum allowable amount.

INTERNET RESOURCE

Remittance Advice Remark Codes

www.wpc-edi.com/codes/remittanceadvice

HEALTH CARE PROVIDER TAXONOMY CODE SET

A **taxonomy code** is a ten-digit number that stands for a physician's medical specialty. The type of specialty may affect the physician's pay. For example, nuclear medicine is usually a higher-paid specialty than internal medicine. An internist who is also certified in nuclear medicine would report the nuclear medicine taxonomy code when billing for that service and use the internal medicine taxonomy code when reporting internal medicine claims. The taxonomy list is maintained by the National Uniform Claim Committee (NUCC).

PLACE OF SERVICE CODES (POS)

Place of service (POS) codes are two-digit codes placed on health care professional claims to indicate the settings in which services were provided. CMS maintains the POS codes used throughout the health care industry. POS codes must be used on professional health care claims from physicians. POS information is often needed to review billing details on claims for services from a provider.

INTERNET RESOURCE

Current Taxonomy Code Set

www.wpc-edi.com/codes/taxonomy

Examples

01 Pharmacy

03 School

11 Office

12 Home

13 Assisted living facility

14 Group home

15 Mobile unit

20 Urgent care facility

21 Inpatient hospital

22 Outpatient hospital

23 Emergency room, hospital

24 Ambulatory surgical center

25 Birthing center

26 Military treatment facility

31 Skilled nursing facility

32 Nursing facility

61 Comprehensive inpatient rehabilitation facility

62 Comprehensive outpatient rehabilitation facility

65 End-stage renal disease treatment facility

71 State or local public health clinic

72 Rural health clinic

81 Independent laboratory

INTERNET RESOURCE

Place of Service Codes

www.cms.hhs.gov/
MedHCPCSGenInfo/
Downloads/Place_of_
Service.pdf

HIPAA National Identifier Standards

HIPAA requires the adoption of unique identifiers for EDI transactions.

EMPLOYER IDENTIFICATION NUMBER (EIN)

The **Employer Identification Number (EIN),** issued by the Internal Revenue Service (IRS), was selected as the identifier for employers effective July 30, 2002. The employer identifier is used when employers enroll or disenroll employees in a health plan (X12 834) or make premium payments to plans on behalf of their employees (X12 820). The EIN is the HIPAA standard.

INTERNET RESOURCE

EIN Regulation

www.cms.hhs.gov/Employer
IdentifierStand/02_Employer
IdentifierRegulations.asp
#TopOfPage

NATIONAL PROVIDER IDENTIFIER (NPI)

The **National Provider Identifier (NPI)** is the standard for the identification of providers for HIPAA transactions. The NPI has replaced other identifying numbers, called **legacy numbers,** that have been in use, such as the UPIN for Medicare and the numbers assigned to providers by payers. (The latest implementation date for NPIs was May 23, 2008, for small health plans.)

The NPI, a unique identification number that is assigned to covered health care providers, is a ten-position, intelligence-free numeric

identifier (a ten-digit number). "Intelligence-free" means that the numbers do not carry other information about health care providers, such as the states in which they live or their medical specialties.

NPIs are assigned by the federal government to individual providers, such as physicians, nurses, dentists, chiropractors, physical therapists, and pharmacists, and also to provider organizations such as hospitals, pharmacies, clinics, group practices, managed care organizations, nursing homes, and laboratories. Once assigned, the NPI does not change; it remains with the provider regardless of job or location changes.

All health care providers who transmit health information electronically must obtain NPIs, even if they use business associates to prepare the transactions, and most health plans—including Medicare, Medicaid, and private payers—and all clearinghouses must now accept and use NPIs in HIPAA transactions.

NATIONAL PLAN AND PROVIDER ENUMERATION SYSTEM (NPPES)

The HIPAA final rule for NPIs established the National Provider System (NPS) to maintain NPIs for all providers. To do so, HHS has set up the **National Plan and Provider Enumeration System (NPPES),** which processes applications for NPIs, assigns them, and then stores the data and identifying numbers for both health plans and providers. NPPES data are available on the Internet; the database can be searched by provider name or number.

4-3   Thinking It Through

A physician practice has sent a bill for a home visit to a patient, but the place of service code is shown as 21. The payer wishes to inform the provider that the amount billed has been reduced because of this problem. What type of administrative code will the payer use? Which code in particular?

CHAPTER REVIEW

CHAPTER SUMMARY

1. The HIPAA Electronic Health Care Transactions and Code Sets and National Identifier standards are being implemented to provide standard formats, code sets, and employer and provider identifiers for exchanging electronic data with efficiency.

2. The eight HIPAA-mandated transactions are (a) health plan premium payments, (b) enrollment or disenrollment in a health plan, (c) eligibility for a health plan, (d) referral certification and authorization, (e) claims, (f) payment/remittance advice, (g) claim status, and (h) coordination of benefits.

3. The Administrative Simplification Compliance Act mandates providers to use the HIPAA electronic claim transaction to bill Medicare unless they are specifically excluded from the requirement.

4. The HIPAA standard code sets for medical code sets are (a) ICD-9-CM Volumes 1 and 2 for diseases; (b) CPT for physician procedures and services; (c) ICD-9-CM Volume 3 for hospital inpatient procedures and services; (d) HCPCS for other supplies and services; (e) CDT codes for dental services; and (f) NDC codes for drugs.

5. ICD-9-CM codes are three-, four-, or five-digit codes describing diseases, injuries, and symptoms. CPT codes are five-digit numbers that describe physicians' services and procedures. HCPCS codes have five digits beginning with a letter and are used for procedures and supplies not found in CPT. ICD-9-CM Volume 3 codes are three- or four-digits long and are used for billing hospital-provider inpatient procedures and services.

6. The sources for up-to-date information on changes to the HIPAA medical code sets for diagnoses and procedures are the CMS website for ICD-9-CM and HCPCS and the American Medical Association website for CPT.

7. The HIPAA-mandated administrative code sets support electronic transactions by standardizing codes to present and explain the information that is exchanged.

8. Changes to the HIPAA administrative code sets are located on the website of the Washington Publishing Company, except for place of service codes, which are located on the CMS website.

9. The HIPAA Employer Identifier standard is the Employer Identification Number (EIN) issued to employers by the Internal Revenue Service.

10. The HIPAA National Provider Identifier, a unique ten-position number assigned to each provider by the federal government, replaces the legacy numbers that have been assigned to providers by various payers in the past.

MATCHING QUESTIONS

Match the key terms with their definitions.

_b_ **1.** administrative code sets

_h_ **2.** medical code sets

_i_ **3.** implementation guide

_c_ **4.** National Provider Identifier

_f_ **5.** legacy identifier

_g_ **6.** claim attachment

_d_ **7.** ICD-9-CM

_e_ **8.** CPT

_j_ **9.** remittance advice

_a_ **10.** HCPCS

a. HIPAA medical code set for supplies

b. HIPAA codes for nonmedical uses

c. HIPAA-assigned unique numbers for doctors, hospitals, and other providers

d. HIPAA-mandated code set for diagnoses

e. HIPAA-mandated code set for procedures

f. Provider identifier formerly assigned by health plans

g. Information to clarify and support a health care claim

h. HIPAA code sets for clinical information

i. Instructions for correct formats for HIPAA transactions

j. Explanation of payment made by a health plan

TRUE/FALSE QUESTIONS

Decide whether each statement is true or false.

_t_ **1.** The number for the HIPAA health care claim transaction is 837.

_f_ **2.** HIPAA-mandated code set use is optional for covered entities.

_t_ **3.** One of the HIPAA transactions is the X12 835 remittance advice that accompanies payments.

_t_ **4.** The Administrative Simplification Compliance Act requires providers to send claims to Medicare electronically unless the providers fall into an exempted category, such as having fewer than ten full-time-equivalent employees.

_f_ **5.** The Eligibility for a Health Plan transaction gives the receiver of a premium payment needed information to properly apply it.

_t_ **6.** CDT is the HIPAA-mandated code set for dental services.

_f_ **7.** CPT codes have five characters.

_T__ **8.** ICD-9-CM codes may have three, four, or five characters.

_F__ **9.** A remittance advice remark code is a type of medical code.

_T__ **10.** A claim status code is sent by a payer to a provider.

MULTIPLE CHOICE QUESTIONS

Select the letter that best completes the statement or answers the question.

1. The HIPAA Electronic Health Care Transactions and Code Sets standards govern

   a. paper transactions

   b. electronic transactions

   c. paper and electronic transactions

   d. none of the above

2. The HIPAA-mandated medical code set for diagnoses, injuries, and symptoms is

   a. ICD-9-CM Volumes 1 and 2

   b. ICD-9-CM Volume 3

   c. CPT

   d. HCPCS

3. The HIPAA-mandated medical code set for hospital inpatient procedures is

   a. ICD-9-CM Volumes 1 and 2

   b. ICD-9-CM Volume 3

   c. CPT

   d. HCPCS

4. The HIPAA-mandated medical code set for physician procedures and services is

   a. ICD-9-CM Volumes 1 and 2

   b. ICD-9-CM Volume 3

   c. CPT

   d. HCPCS

5. The HIPAA-mandated medical code set for supplies is

   a. ICD-9-CM Volumes 1 and 2

   b. ICD-9-CM Volume 3

   c. CPT

   d. HCPCS

6. Which of the following transactions *does not* flow between the provider and the payer?

   a. Health Plan Premium Payments

   b. Health Care Claim Status

   c. Health Care Payment and Remittance Advice

   d. Health Care Claims

7. The Administrative Simplification Compliance Act requires electronic claims to be submitted to

   a. private payers

   b. Medicare

   c. both A and B

   d. neither A nor B

8. On compliant HIPAA transactions, which of the following can be used to identify a provider?

   a. NPI

   b. legacy number

   c. NPI and legacy number

   d. none of the above

9. The list of national provider identifier numbers can be accessed on the website of

   a. DSMO

   b. NPPES

   c. EIN

   d. WPC

10. The Functional Acknowledgment confirms that an electronic message

    a. has been received

    b. has been sent

    c. has been received without transmission errors

    d. none of the above

SHORT ANSWER QUESTIONS

Define the following abbreviations.

1. CPT Current Procedural Terminology

2. ICD-9-CM International Classification of Diseases 9 revision Clinical Modifica

3. RA remittance advice

4. EIN Employer Identification Number

5. NPI National Provider Identifier

APPLYING YOUR KNOWLEDGE

HIPAA Cases

For each of the following events, assign a HIPAA transaction number.

1. A payer transfers money to a physician's practice bank and explains the amount of the payment in an explanation of benefits.

2. A hospital transmits a claim to a payer for a patient's ten-day hospitalization.

3. A medical insurance specialist follows up with the payer on a late claim by transmitting a query.

4. A health plan cannot find a particular patient for whom a claim has been transmitted in its system, so it sends a query to the provider that sent the claim.

5. A family physician sends a query to the patient's health plan requesting a referral number for a cardiac specialist.

HIPAA Communications

1. A gynecologist sends this e-mail message to the office manager: *Please find out if Susan Billing is eligible for a cesarean section under her health plan.* What kind of HIPAA transaction will the office manager prepare? What kind of medical code will be used to indicate the kind of service that is being queried?

2. An inpatient billing department of a hospital is gathering information to bill a patient's health plan for a recent stay for open-heart surgery. What kind of HIPAA transaction will the biller prepare? What kind of medical code will be used to report the procedure the patient underwent?

RESEARCHING THE INTERNET

1. Using a web browser such as Google or Yahoo!, locate the home page for the NEPPS—the National Plan and Provider Enumeration System—and research the NPIs that have been assigned to local providers in your area.

2. Visit the website for information about ICD-10-CM at www.cdc. gov/nchs/about/otheract/icd9/icd10cm.htm and report on the current status of this code set.

5

HIPAA Enforcement

CHAPTER OUTLINE

LEARNING OUTCOMES

After studying this chapter, you should be able to:

1. Explain the purpose of the HIPAA final enforcement rule.
2. Distinguish between civil and criminal cases.
3. Describe the roles of the Office for Civil Rights (OCR) and the Department of Justice (DOJ) in the enforcement of the HIPAA privacy standards.
4. Describe the role of the Centers for Medicare and Medicaid Services (CMS) in the enforcement of the HIPAA security, transactions, code sets, and identifiers standards.
5. Describe the civil case procedure followed by OCR and CMS.

6. Discuss the role of the Office of Inspector General (OIG) of the Health and Human Services Department (HHS) in enforcing HIPAA.
7. Compare fraud and abuse.
8. Discuss the laws that underpin the OIG's fraud and abuse enforcement actions.
9. Describe the purpose of an OIG Work Plan.
10. List the recommended elements of a compliance plan.

KEY TERMS

abuse
administrative law judge (ALJ)
advisory opinion
audit
audit reports
benchmark
certification of compliance agreement (CCA)
civil money penalties (CMP)
civil violation
code of conduct
compliance plan
compliance program guidance
corporate integrity agreement (CIA)
criminal violation
Deficit Reduction Act (DRA) of 2005
Department of Justice (DOJ)

excluded parties
external audit
False Claims Act (FCA)
fraud
Health Care Fraud and Abuse Control Program
HIPAA final enforcement rule
internal audit
Office of the Inspector General (OIG)
OIG Fraud Alert
OIG Work Plan
qui tam
relator
Stark II
triggered reviews
upcoding

Why This Chapter Is Important

Enforcement of the HIPAA privacy, security, transactions, and identifier standards, as well as of related fraud and abuse laws, has a significant effect on the daily activities of allied health employees in all health care settings. It is important to be aware of the serious nature of penalties for violations of applicable laws and to understand the steps that can be taken to avoid even the suggestion of improper conduct as an employee.

Think about the following case as you study the HIPAA final enforcement rule. In your opinion, is the punishment too severe for the action? Decide on your answer, and compare it with the case discussion that precedes the chapter summary.

> More than 100 employees of a local clinic in Minnesota were suspended this year for violating federal laws on patient privacy—mostly by tapping into electronic records of relatives or friends, according to clinic officials.
>
> The clinic notified its 8,300 employees about the suspensions as a reminder of what it calls its "zero tolerance policy" on confidentiality. Employees are told about the policy when they first apply for jobs, and reminders are regularly issued.
>
> Already, twice as many employees have been disciplined for privacy violations in 2007 than in all of 2006, officials say. They were suspended without pay for three days.
>
> "Anyone that has anything to do with patient care, from scheduling appointments to actually performing patient care, has access to the medical record," said the corporation's attorney, who wrote the e-mail to the clinic staff. "That's why we take it so seriously. In many cases, employees have been tempted to peek at charts of neighbors or family members—a case of 'old habits die hard.'"

The HIPAA Final Enforcement Rule

The **HIPAA final enforcement rule** became law and was required to be implemented on March 16, 2006. Unlike previous HIPAA rules, the final enforcement rule did not provide covered entities (CEs) with the usual two-year period to prepare. Covered entities had been aware of the basic enforcement provisions that each published standard had contained, so they did not need a long lead time to prepare for enforcement.

The purpose of the HIPAA final enforcement rule is to reconcile differences in enforcement procedures that had existed between the privacy and the security standards by imposing a single rule. It makes clear that both *acts*—things that are done—and *omissions*—things that are not done, like failure to implement a particular provision—may be HIPAA violations. All Administrative Simplification provisions legislated under HIPAA are currently covered under this final enforcement rule.

The complete rule as published in the *Federal Register* is available via the Department of Health and Human Services (HHS) Office for Civil Rights HIPAA home page, as shown in Figure 5-1.

HIPAA ENFORCEMENT AGENCIES

Enforcing HIPAA is the job of a number of government agencies. Which agency performs which task depends on the nature of the violation.

Figure 5-1

Final Enforcement Rule
Published on OCR HIPAA
Home Page

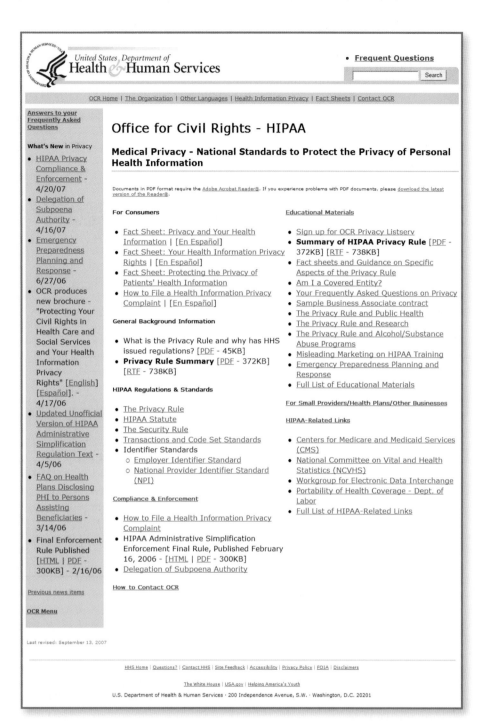

Office for Civil Rights

Civil violations of the HIPAA privacy standards are enforced by the Office for Civil Rights (OCR), an agency of HHS. OCR has the authority to receive and investigate complaints as well as to issue subpoenas for evidence in cases it is investigating. It is charged with enforcing the privacy standards because privacy is considered a civil right. It is important to note, though, that individuals themselves do not have the right to sue a covered entity that may have disclosed their PHI inappropriately; action must be taken on individuals' behalf by the OCR. The OCR's compliance and enforcement home page is shown in Figure 5-2 on page 118.

FYI

Civil or Criminal?

Violations of HIPAA may be civil offenses, or they may be criminal in nature. A **civil violation** is based on civil law. Such a violation, which is handled in some kind of a legal court system, begins with a person's entering a complaint against another person or entity, usually asking for some kind of remedy such as a financial payment. Examples of general civil cases are trespassing suits, divorce proceedings, and breach of contract proceedings. A **criminal violation,** on the other hand, is based on a branch of the law that defines crime—such as kidnapping, robbery, and arson—and provides for its punishment. A criminal violation is regarded as an offense committed against the public, even though only one individual may have been wronged, and the wrongdoer is prosecuted by the government for the purpose of punishment, which may include a financial penalty and a prison sentence.

Figure 5-2
OCR HIPAA Compliance and Enforcement Home Page

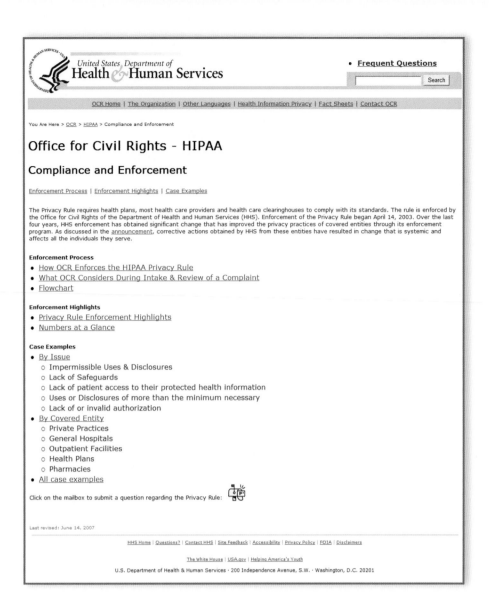

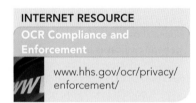

Department of Justice

Criminal violations of HIPAA privacy standards are prosecuted by the federal government's **Department of Justice (DOJ).** As America's "law office" and central agency for enforcement of federal laws, the stated task of the DOJ is:

> To enforce the law and defend the interests of the United States according to the law; to ensure public safety against threats foreign and domestic; to provide federal leadership in preventing and controlling crime; to seek just punishment for those guilty of unlawful behavior; and to ensure fair and impartial administration of justice for all Americans.

Centers for Medicare and Medicaid Services

All the nonprivacy standards are enforced by the Centers for Medicare and Medicaid Services (CMS). Also an agency of HHS, CMS has the major task of administering the Medicare and Medicaid programs.

HHS has also authorized CMS to investigate complaints of noncompliance and enforce these HIPAA standards:

> The Electronic Health Care Transaction and Code Set Rule (TCS)

> The National Employer Identifier Number (EIN) Rule

> The Security Rule

> The National Provider Identifier Rule

> The National Plan Identifier Rule (currently under development)

Figure 5-3 shows the CMS HIPAA enforcement home page.

INTERNET RESOURCE
CMS HIPAA Enforcement
www.cms.hhs.gov/
Enforcement/

Office of Inspector General

A fourth government group, the **Office of Inspector General (OIG),** a part of HHS, was directed by the original HIPAA law (the Health Insurance Portability and Accountability Act of 1996) to combat fraud and abuse in health insurance and health care delivery. Every federal agency has its own inspector general who is responsible for uncovering fraudulent actions in the agency's programs. The HHS OIG is particularly important, since it is authorized to oversee the federal government Medicare and Medicaid insurance programs. Providers and health plans that participate in Medicare and Medicaid are required to provide the government with the records that support

Figure 5-3
CMS Enforcement Home Page

Figure 5-4
OIG Home Page

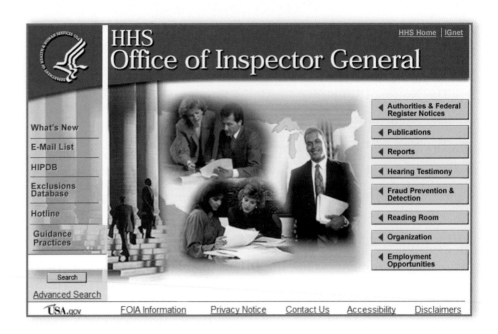

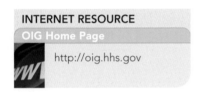

billing of these programs. The OIG has the authority to review and investigate these records and can issue subpoenas and gain access to medical records.

Figure 5-4 shows the OIG home page.

CIVIL CASE PROCEDURES

For civil cases, the enforcing agency must receive and then accept a complaint. If a complaint is related to privacy or security, usually the complainer is a patient. The recommended privacy compliant form is shown in Figure 5-5. The OCR has reported the following as the top five complaints:

1. Improper use or disclosure of an individual's protected health information (PHI)

2. Inadequate safeguards of PHI

3. Failure to provide individuals with access to their records

4. Disclosure of more than minimally necessary

5. Failure to obtain authorization for a disclosure that requires it

If a complaint involves transactions, code sets, or identifiers, the complainer is often another CE that does business with the CE that complains. For example, a health plan may file a complaint about a provider that is not submitting HIPAA-compliant transactions such as claims. Figure 5-6 on page 123–125 shows the three-page HIPAA non-privacy complaint form.

If a complaint is accepted for investigation, the agency notifies the person who filed it as well as the covered entity that is named as the violator. Both the filer and the CE are then asked to submit information.

Form Approved: OMB No. 0990-0269
See OMB Statement on Reverse.

DEPARTMENT OF HEALTH AND HUMAN SERVICES
OFFICE FOR CIVIL RIGHTS (OCR)

HEALTH INFORMATION PRIVACY COMPLAINT

If you have questions about this form, call OCR (toll-free) at:
1-800-368-1019 (any language) or 1-800-537-7697 (TDD)

YOUR FIRST NAME	YOUR LAST NAME

HOME PHONE ( )	WORK PHONE ( )

STREET ADDRESS		CITY

STATE	ZIP	E-MAIL ADDRESS *(If available)*

Are you filing this complaint for someone else? ☐ Yes ☐ No

If Yes, whose health information privacy rights do you believe were violated?

FIRST NAME	LAST NAME

Who (or what agency or organization, e.g., provider, health plan) do you believe violated your (or someone else's) health information privacy rights or committed another violation of the Privacy Rule?

PERSON/AGENCY/ORGANIZATION

STREET ADDRESS	CITY

STATE	ZIP	PHONE ( )

When do you believe that the violation of health information privacy rights occurred?

LIST DATE(S)

Describe briefly what happened. How and why do you believe your (or someone else's) health information privacy rights were violated, or the privacy rule otherwise was violated? Please be as specific as possible. *(Attach additional pages as needed)*

Please sign and date this complaint.

SIGNATURE	DATE

Filing a complaint with OCR is voluntary. However, without the information requested above, OCR may be unable to proceed with your complaint. We collect this information under authority of the Privacy Rule issued pursuant to the Health Insurance Portability and Accountability Act of 1996. We will use the information you provide to determine if we have jurisdiction and, if so, how we will process your complaint. Information submitted on this form is treated confidentially and is protected under the provisions of the Privacy Act of 1974. Names or other identifying information about individuals are disclosed when it is necessary for investigation of possible health information privacy violations, for internal systems operations, or for routine uses, which include disclosure of information outside the Department for purposes associated with health information privacy compliance and as permitted by law. It is illegal for a covered entity to intimidate, threaten, coerce, discriminate or retaliate against you for filing this complaint or for taking any other action to enforce your rights under the Privacy Rule. You are not required to use this form. You also may write a letter or submit a complaint electronically with the same information. To submit an electronic complaint, go to our web site at: **www.hhs.gov/ocr/privacyhowtofile.html.** To mail a complaint see reverse page for OCR Regional addresses.

HHS-700 (4/03) (FRONT)

Figure 5-5

Health Information Privacy Complaint (a) front

(The remaining information on this form is optional. Failure to answer these voluntary questions will not affect OCR's decision to process your complaint.)

Do you need special accommodations for us to communicate with you about this complaint (check all that apply)?

☐ Braille ☐ Large Print ☐ Cassette tape ☐ Computer diskette ☐ Electronic mail ☐ TDD

☐ Sign language interpreter *(specify language)*: _____

☐ Foreign language interpreter *(specify language)*: _____ ☐ Other: _____

If we cannot reach you directly, is there someone we can contact to help us reach you?

FIRST NAME | LAST NAME

HOME PHONE | WORK PHONE
( ) | ( )

STREET ADDRESS | CITY

STATE | ZIP | E-MAIL ADDRESS *(If available)*

Have you filed your complaint anywhere else? If so, please provide the following. (Attach additional pages as needed.)
PERSON / AGENCY / ORGANIZATION / COURT NAME(S)

DATE(S) FILED | CASE NUMBER(S) *(If known)*

To help us better serve the public, please provide the following information for the person you believe had their health information privacy rights violated (you or the person on whose behalf you are filing).

ETHNICITY *(select one)*   RACE *(select one or more)*

☐ Hispanic or Latino   ☐ American Indian or Alaska Native   ☐ Asian   ☐ Native Hawaiian or Other Pacific Islander

☐ Not Hispanic or Latino   ☐ Black or African American   ☐ White   ☐ Other *(specify)*: _____

PRIMARY LANGUAGE SPOKEN *(if other then English)* | HOW DID YOU LEARN ABOUT THE OFFICE FOR CIVIL RIGHTS?

To mail a complaint, please type or print, and return completed complaint to the OCR Regional Address based on the region where the alleged discrimination took place.

Region I - CT, ME, MA, NH, RI, VT	**Region V - IL, IN, MI, MN, OH, WI**	**Region IX - AZ, CA, HI, NV, AS, GU, The U.S. Affiliated Pacific Island Jurisdictions**
Office for Civil Rights Department of Health & Human Services JFK Federal Building - Room 1875 Boston, MA 02203 (617) 565-1340; (617) 565-1343 (TDD) (617) 565-3809 FAX	Office for Civil Rights Department of Health & Human Services 233 N. Michigan Ave. - Suite 240 Chicago, IL 60601 (312) 886-2359; (312) 353-5693 (TDD) (312) 886-1807 FAX	Office for Civil Rights Department of Health & Human Services 50 United Nations Plaza - Room 322 San Francisco, CA 94102 (415) 437-8310; (415) 437-8311 (TDD) (415) 437-8329 FAX
Region II - NJ, NY, PR, VI Office for Civil Rights Department of Health & Human Services 26 Federal Plaza - Suite 3313 New York, NY 10278 (212) 264-3313; (212) 264-2355 (TDD) (212) 264-3039 FAX	**Region VI - AR, LA, NM, OK, TX** Office for Civil Rights Department of Health & Human Services 1301 Young Street - Suite 1169 Dallas, TX 75202 (214) 767-4056; (214) 767-8940 (TDD) (214) 767-0432 FAX	
Region III - DE, DC, MD, PA, VA, WV Office for Civil Rights Department of Health & Human Services 150 S. Independence Mall West - Suite 372 Philadelphia, PA 19106-3499 (215) 861-4441; (215) 861-4440 (TDD) (215) 861-4431 FAX	**Region VII - IA, KS, MO, NE** Office for Civil Rights Department of Health & Human Services 601 East 12th Street - Room 248 Kansas City, MO 64106 (816) 426-7278; (816) 426-7065 (TDD) (816) 426-3686 FAX	**Region X - AK, ID, OR, WA** Office for Civil Rights Department of Health & Human Services 2201 Sixth Avenue - Mail Stop RX-11 Seattle, WA 98121 (206) 615-2290; (206) 615-2296 (TDD) (206) 615-2297 FAX
Region IV - AL, FL, GA, KY, MS, NC, SC, TN Office for Civil Rights Department of Health & Human Services 61 Forsyth Street, SW. - Suite 3B70 Atlanta, GA 30323 (404) 562-7886; (404) 331-2867 (TDD) (404) 562-7881 FAX	**Region VIII - CO, MT, ND, SD, UT, WY** Office for Civil Rights Department of Health & Human Services 1961 Stout Street - Room 1426 Denver, CO 80294 (303) 844-2024; (303) 844-3439 (TDD) (303) 844-2025 FAX	

Burden Statement

Public reporting burden for the collection of information on this complaint form is estimated to average 45 minutes per response, including the time for reviewing instructions, gathering the data needed and entering and reviewing the information on the completed complaint form. An agency may not conduct or sponsor, and a person is not required to respond to, a collection of information unless it displays a valid control number. Send comments regarding this burden estimate or any other aspect of this collection of information, including suggestions for reducing this burden, to: HHS/OS Reports Clearance Officer, Office of Information Resources Management, 200 Independence Ave. S.W., Room 531H, Washington, D.C. 20201.

HHS-700 (4/03) (BACK)

Figure 5-5

(Continued) (b) back

Form Approved: OMB # 0938-0948

Centers for Medicare & Medicaid Services (CMS)
Office of E-Health Standards and Services (OESS)
HIPAA Non-Privacy Complaint Form

IMPORTANT: This form cannot be used for HIPAA Privacy complaints. Please direct privacy complaints to the Office for Civil Rights at 1-800-368-1019 or visit their website: www.hhs.gov/ocr/hipaa

If you have any general questions about the HIPAA Regulations visit our website at:
www.cms.hhs.gov

Please provide your contact information: (All fields required.)

YOUR NAME (First and Last)		ORGANIZATION NAME	
STREET ADDRESS		TELEPHONE NUMBER	
CITY/TOWN	COUNTY	STATE	ZIP

Who (or what agency/organization, e.g. health care clearinghouse, health plan, or covered health care provider) are you filing this complaint against? (All fields required.)

ORGANIZATION NAME		CONTACT NAME	
STREET ADDRESS		TELEPHONE NUMBER	
CITY/TOWN	COUNTY	STATE	ZIP

When did this alleged violation occur? mm/dd/yyyy (Required field.)

Identify the HIPAA Non-Privacy complaint category? (Required field.) Select one regulatory category listed below per complaint submission. Complete this form again to file a complaint for another category listed below.

☐   **Transactions and Code Sets**   ☐   **Unique Identifiers**   ☐   **Security Standards**

Describe, in detail, the alleged violation. (Required field.) You may attach additional pages as needed. Please enclose copies of any additional documents (e.g. companion guide, security risk assessment) that may help OESS resolve your complaint.

Please Print or Type.

Please sign and date this complaint. (Required field.)
SIGNATURE: DATE:

Filing a complaint with CMS is voluntary. However, without the information requested on the complaint form, CMS may be unable to proceed with a complaint. CMS collects this information under authority of 68 FR 60694 (October 23, 2003) issued pursuant to the HIPAA. CMS will use the information provided to determine if CMS has jurisdiction and, if so, how CMS will process the complaint. Information submitted on the complaint form is treated confidentially and is protected under the provisions of the Privacy Act of 1974. Names or other identifying information about individuals are disclosed only when it is necessary for investigation of possible HIPAA A.S. Non-Privacy violations, for internal systems operations, or for routine uses, which include disclosure of information outside the Department for purposes associated with HIPAA A.S. Non-Privacy compliance and as permitted by law. To submit an electronic complaint, go to our web site at: http://htct.hhs.gov

Figure 5-6

HIPAA Non-Privacy Complaint Form

Centers for Medicare & Medicaid Services (CMS)
Office of E-Health Standards and Services (OESS)
HIPAA Non-Privacy Complaint Form

IMPORTANT: The information requested in the remainder of the is form is optional. However, any additional information you provide will assist OESS in the enforcement process.

OPTIONAL INFORMATION

Have you filed this complaint with another agency? If so, please provide us with the following:

Agency Name:	Agency Contact Person:
Date the Complaint was Filed:	Contact Number:
Complaint Identification Number:	

Please provide OESS with more detail about this complaint.

1. **Please describe yourself.**
   - ❑ Health Plan
   - ❑ Covered Health Care Provider (*See examples on the right*)
   - ❑ Health Care Clearinghouse
   - ❑ Patient or representative of the patient
   - ❑ Other:_____

2. **Who are you filing this complaint against?**
   - ❑ Health Plan
   - ❑ Covered Health Care Provider (*See examples on the right*)
   - ❑ Health Care Clearinghouse

3. **Have you attempted to resolve the dispute?**
   - ❑ YES
   - ❑ NO

Examples of Covered Health Care Providers:
Ambulance Service
Comprehensive Outpatient Rehabilitation Facility
Durable Medical Equipment Service
Home Health Agency
Hospice Program
Hospital / Critical Access Hospital
Non-Physician Practitioners
Outpatient Physical or Occupational Therapy
Physician
Rural Health Clinics and Federally Qualified Health Centers
Skilled Nursing Facility

For a Transactions and Code Sets Complaint (Check the appropriate box.)

❑ **Non-Compliant Transaction Received** - You received a non-compliant HIPAA transaction from a covered entity.

❑ **Compliant Transaction Sent and Rejected** - A covered entity rejected your compliant HIPAA transaction.

❑ **Invalid Companion Guide** - A covered entity that you send data to or receive data from requires uses of a non-compliant companion guide. For example, a companion guide must not specify additional fields beyond those specified by HIPAA.

❑ **Code Set Received or Sent and Rejected**: - Either or both of these examples may apply: (1) A covered entity sent you a non-compliant HIPAA code within an electronic transaction. (2) A covered entity rejected a compliant HIPAA code that you sent within an electronic transaction.

❑ **Other** - You have another type of complaint against a covered entity.

Disclosure Statement: According to the Paperwork Reduction Act of 1995, no persons are required to respond to a collection of information unless it displays a valid OMB control number. The valid OMB control number for this information collection is **0938-0948**. The time required to complete this information collection is estimated to average **1 hour per** response, including the time to review instructions, search existing data resources, gather the data needed, and complete and review the information collection. If you have comments, concerning the accuracy of the time estimate(s) or suggestions for improving this form, please write to: CMS, 7500 Security Boulevard, Attn: PRA Reports Clearance Officer, Baltimore, Maryland 21244-1850.

Figure 5-6
(*Continued*)

Centers for Medicare & Medicaid Services (CMS)
Office of E-Health Standards and Services (OESS)
HIPAA Non-Privacy Complaint Form

IMPORTANT: The information requested in the remainder of the is form is optional. However, any additional information you provide will assist OESS in the enforcement process.

OPTIONAL INFORMATION

For a Transactions and Code Sets Complaint (Check the appropriate box.)

1. **Check the appropriate transaction(s) discussed in your complaint. Note: If your complaint involves a transaction(s) that is not listed, you may not have a valid transaction complaint.**

❑ 270 Eligibility, Coverage or Benefit Inquiry	❑ 837 Health Care Claim: Dental	❑ 835 Health Care Claim Payment/Advice
❑ 271 Eligibility, Coverage or Benefit Information	❑ 837 Health Care Claim – Professional	❑ 820 Payment Order/Remittance Advice
❑ 276 Health Care Claim Status Request	❑ 837 Health Care Claim: Institutional	❑ 278 Health Care Services Review - Request for Review
❑ 277 Health Care Claim Status Notification	❑ 834 Benefit Enrollment and Maintenance	❑ 278 Health Care Services Review - Response to Request for Review
❑ NCPDP Retail Pharmacy Transactions	❑ I don't know	

2. **Check the appropriate code set(s) discussed in your complaint.**

❑ International Classification of Diseases, 9th Edition, Clinical Modification (ICD-9-CM)	❑ Healthcare Common Procedure Coding System (HCPCS)
❑ Common Procedure Terminology (CPT)	❑ National Drug Code (NDC)
❑ Codes on Dental Procedures and Nomenclature - Current Dental Terminology (CDT)	❑ Other:_____

For a Security Complaint (Check the appropriate box.)

Do you believe that personal health information was wrongfully shared or disclosed, or that the action you are complaining about otherwise violated the health information Privacy Rule?

❑ YES

❑ NO

Mail completed forms to: **Centers for Medicare & Medicaid Services**
HIPAA TCS Enforcement Activities
P.O. Box 8030
Baltimore, Maryland 21244-8030

Figure 5-6
(Continued)

CEs are required by law to cooperate with complaint investigations. When the OCR or CMS investigates a complaint, the CE must provide access to its facilities, books, records, and systems, including relevant protected health information. The OCR also has the authority to issue subpoenas in investigations of alleged violations of the Privacy Rule. These subpoenas require witnesses to appear as required, to testify, and to provide requested evidence relating to the failure to comply with the rule.

The enforcing agency reviews the facts of the case. It may determine that the CE did not violate HIPAA requirements. If the evidence indicates that the CE was in violation, the agency attempts to resolve the case with the CE by obtaining voluntary compliance, corrective action, or other resolution.

Voluntary Compliance

The HIPAA Administrative Simplification provisions are based on the idea that CEs will work toward voluntary compliance. The government's chief weapon that encourages voluntary action is publicity. If an organization or physician is found to be out of compliance, HHS notifies the public as well as appropriate organizations and entities. These include:

> State or local medical or professional organizations

> State agencies that administer or supervise state health care programs

> Organizations that perform peer review and quality control of providers

> State or local licensing agencies

Since bad publicity has a negative effect on patients' opinions of the covered entity, most CEs take steps to avoid noncompliance. In keeping with this approach, HHS helps CEs with education and advice on compliant procedures.

Civil Money Penalties

Most privacy complaints have been settled by voluntary compliance. But if the covered entity does not act to resolve the matter in a way that is satisfactory, the enforcing agency can impose **civil money penalties (CMPs).** The ability to impose CMPs is limited, however. First, a CMP may not be imposed for cases involving criminal penalties. Second, a CMP may not be imposed if the CE liable for the penalty did not know, and by exercising reasonable diligence would not have known, that it was in violation. Third, a CMP may not be imposed if the failure to comply was due "to reasonable cause and not to willful neglect" and is corrected within a certain time. Finally, a CMP may be reduced or waived entirely if it is judged to be excessive relative to the compliance failure involved.

The final enforcement rule establishes civil money penalties of not more than $100 for each violation and not more than $25,000 for all violations of identical type during a single calendar year.

If CMPs are imposed, the covered entity may challenge them by requesting a hearing in which an HHS **administrative law judge (ALJ)** decides whether the penalties are supported by the evidence. The CE also has the right to appeal the ALJ's decision. The person who filed the complaint does not receive a portion of CMPs collected from CEs; the penalties are deposited in the U.S. Treasury.

CRIMINAL CASE PROCEDURES

If the OCR or CMS receives a complaint that may lead to a criminal case, the agency will usually refer the complaint to the DOJ for investigation. For criminal cases, such as for selling unique health identifiers for identity theft purposes, these penalties can be imposed:

	FINE	PRISON
Knowingly obtaining PHI in violation of HIPAA	$50,000	1 year
Offenses done under false pretenses	$100,000	5 years
Using PHI for profit, gain, or harm	$250,000	10 years

Figure 5-7 shows a flow chart for the complaint process. The starting point is the receipt of a complaint by the OCR.

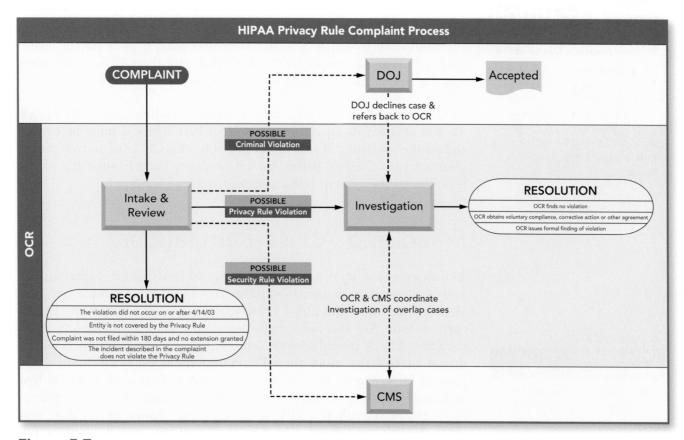

Figure 5-7

HIPAA Complaint Process

In the first four years of implementation, more than 24,000 privacy complaints were lodged with the OCR, but no CMPs were issued. Is this lack of monetary fines a sign of effective enforcement?

WHO IS RESPONSIBLE: THE COVERED ENTITY, BUSINESS ASSOCIATES, OR EMPLOYEES?

It is important to note that only covered entities—not employees or business associates (BAs)—can be charged with HIPAA violations, and that only the enforcing agencies—not individuals—can bring the charges. In the case of criminal violations, while HIPAA gives the government authority to prosecute CEs for criminal violations, employees are not automatically covered by the law and may not be subject to criminal penalties. But depending on the facts of a particular case, certain employees may be directly liable under other laws, like corporate criminal liability laws.

Also important are the rules governing reporting of violations by a CE's employees or its business associates. An employee of the CE or its BAs who believes in good faith that the CE has engaged in conduct that is unlawful, violates professional or clinical standards, or endangers patients, other workers, or the public may disclose protected health information (PHI) without violating HIPAA. The individual must make the disclosure to either a health oversight agency or a public health authority that has responsibility for regulating the CE, or to an attorney the individual has hired for legal advice on the situation.

Similarly, there are rules for the CE to follow when a business associate has violated its agreement to protect PHI. The CE must take steps to end the violation; if this is not possible, the CE must terminate the contract with the BA. If this cannot be done, the CE must report the problem to the appropriate enforcing agency.

Fraud and Abuse Regulations

Almost everyone involved in the delivery of health care is trustworthy and is devoted to patients' welfare. However, some people are not. Health care fraud and abuse laws help control cheating in the health care system. Are the laws really necessary? The evidence says that they are. The National Health Care Anti-Fraud Association has estimated that of the more than $2 trillion spent on health care every year, at least 3 percent—or more than $60 billion each year—is lost to fraud. This loss directly affects patients, taxpayers, and government through higher health care costs, insurance premiums, and taxes. Health care fraud also may hurt patients, possibly subjecting some of them to unnecessary or unsafe procedures or making them victims of identity theft.

HIPAA ⚠ CAUTION

Include Security Provisions in Business Associate Agreements

Recommended practice is to include security controls in BA agreements and to require the BA to conduct ongoing security audits.

HIPAA ⚠ CAUTION

Business Associate Misuse of PHI

CEs that are aware of misuse of PHI by a business associate must take reasonable steps to fix the breach or break the BA agreement. If these steps are not possible, the CE must report the breach to the Office for Civil Rights.

COMPLIANCE TIP

HIPAA Violations and Fraud Cases

HSS can use information from HIPAA privacy-, security-, and transactions-related investigations in investigating the possibility of fraud.

THE HEALTH CARE FRAUD AND ABUSE CONTROL PROGRAM

HIPAA created the **Health Care Fraud and Abuse Control Program** to uncover and prosecute fraud and abuse. The HHS OIG has the task of detecting health care fraud and abuse and enforcing all laws relating to them. The OIG works with the DOJ under the direction of the U.S. attorney general to prosecute those suspected of medical fraud and abuse.

FEDERAL FALSE CLAIMS ACT

The federal **False Claims Act** (**FCA,** 31 USC § 3729) prohibits submitting a fraudulent claim or making a false statement or representation in connection with a claim. It also encourages reporting suspected fraud and abuse against the government by protecting and rewarding people involved in *qui tam,* or whistle-blower, cases. The person who makes the accusation of suspected fraud is called the **relator.** Under the law, the relator is protected against employer retaliation. If the lawsuit results in a fine paid to the federal government, the whistle-blower may be entitled to 15 to 25 percent of the amount paid. People who blow the whistle are current or former employees of insurance companies or medical practices, program beneficiaries, and independent contractors.

ADDITIONAL LAWS

Additional laws relate to health care fraud and abuse control.

Antikickback Act of 1986

An antikickback statute makes it illegal to knowingly offer incentives to induce referrals for services that are paid by government health care programs. Many financial actions are considered to be incentives, including illegal direct payments to other physicians and routine waivers of coinsurance and deductibles.

Stark Laws

Under the federal law governing *self-referrals*, a physician cannot (1) refer patients to an entity (2) for the furnishing of designated health services (3) if there is a financial relationship between the referring physician (or an immediate family member of the referring physician) and the entity, (4) unless the financial relationship fits within one of the specific exceptions in the statute or regulations. Designated health services include clinical laboratory services; physical therapy, occupational therapy, and speech-language pathology services; radiology and certain other imaging services; radiation therapy services and supplies; durable medical equipment and supplies; parenteral and enteral nutrients, equipment, and supplies; prosthetics, orthotics, and prosthetic devices and supplies; home health services; outpatient prescription drugs; and inpatient and outpatient hospital services.

HIPAA created a new category of crimes that apply to billing transactions with private payers in addition to Medicare and Medicaid billing. These offenses include health care fraud, making false statements, theft and embezzlement, obstruction of criminal investigations, and money laundering.

The laws are called "Stark I" and "Stark II." The original Stark law (Stark I), enacted in 1989, prohibited only self-interested referrals for clinical laboratory services. In 1993, Congress broadened the Stark law (Stark II) to include referrals of a broad array of designated health services. In general, **Stark II** is enforced in conjunction with other federal laws, including the antikickback statute. Stark II presently provides for civil money penalties not to exceed $100,000 for each "arrangement or scheme" that a person knows or should know has a principal purpose to violate the statute. Additionally, the government may withhold payments for prohibited referrals or seek to recoup past payments.

Sarbanes-Oxley Act

The Sarbanes-Oxley Act of 2002 requires publicly traded corporations to attest that their financial management is sound. These provisions apply to for-profit health care companies. The act includes whistle-blower protection so that employees can report wrongdoing without fear of retaliation.

Deficit Reduction Act

The **Deficit Reduction Act (DRA) of 2005** gave OIG new authority to review and evaluate (1) state false claims laws, (2) the compliance plans of prescription drug plan sponsors, (3) reported deaths of patients in restraint or seclusion, and (4) the responses of public health personnel to the emergencies created by Hurricanes Katrina and Rita. The DRA has financial incentives for states to pass their own false claims acts that provide for whistle-blower protections, reward whistle-blowers, and do not require proof of intent to defraud for prosecution to go ahead. This act also requires large hospitals and nursing homes to teach employees to recognize and report fraud.

DEFINITION OF FRAUD AND ABUSE

Fraud is an act of deception to take financial advantage of another person. Fraudulent acts are intentional; the individual expects an illegal or unauthorized benefit to result. For example, misrepresenting professional credentials and forging another person's signature on a check are fraudulent. These are other examples of actual cases:

> A major corporation paid the federal government a record-setting $54 million as part of an ongoing criminal and civil investigation of alleged unnecessary cardiac procedures and surgeries. The case involved allegations of unnecessary procedures, tests, lab studies, and surgeries. The corporation agreed to random audits of cardiology procedures to be held twice yearly and other measures to ensure compliance.

> A pharmacy billed for HIV medications that were not needed by patients.

> A provider billed health plans for drug samples that the physicians received for free.

> **Upcoding** office visits—meaning transmitting false claims that reported more intensive patient examinations than were performed—was done by a provider.

> A provider billed health plans for services that were not performed.

> Stolen patient information ended up on fake Medicare claims.

> Patients exaggerated injuries to get settlements from insurance companies.

In federal law, **abuse** means actions that are not sound medical, business, or fiscal practices and that misuse money that the government has allocated, such as Medicare funds. Abuse is illegal because taxpayers' dollars are misspent. An example of abuse is an ambulance service that billed Medicare for transporting a patient to the hospital when the patient did not need ambulance service. This abuse—billing for services that were not medically necessary—resulted in improper payment to the ambulance company. Abuse is not necessarily intentional. It may be the result of ignorance of a billing rule or of inaccurate coding.

OIG INVESTIGATIONS , AUDITS, AND ADVICE

OIG has the authority to investigate suspected fraud cases and to review the records of covered entities. A number of investigative tools are associated with the OIG.

The OIG Work Plan

Each year, as part of a Medicare Fraud and Abuse Initiative, the OIG announces the **OIG Work Plan.** The Work Plan lists the year's planned projects for sampling particular types of billing to see if there are problems. These projects may address any area of health care billing and finance, including physicians, hospitals, long-term care facilities, and other settings.

OIG Work Plans point to the areas on which government investigations will focus. Covered entities, particularly the compliance officers CEs appoint to keep current with changing regulations, study these initiatives and make sure their procedures comply with the existing rules.

Advisory Opinions

At times, efforts to be in compliance can be problematic. Some regulations are contradictory or unclear, and some are too new to be well understood. For help, both the OIG and CMS issue **advisory opinions** on various questions. These opinions are legal advice only for the requesting parties, who, if they act according to the advice, cannot be investigated on the matter. To receive an advisory opinion, an individual, such as a physician, or a legal entity, such as a hospital, formally presents a situation and asks whether the way it intends to handle the situation is fraudulent. CMS or the OIG responds with an opinion. Although taking this advice legally protects only the party that asks the question, the answers are valuable to everyone who has an interest in the subject.

The following example is taken from an OIG advisory opinion. (When advisory opinions are published, the names of the parties are *redacted*—removed from the public document—to keep that information private.) In this situation, the parties asked for the OIG's opinion on a business arrangement that they were concerned might be investigated as fraud:

> We are writing in response to your request for an advisory opinion, in which you asked whether an arrangement whereby an independent physician association would acquire an equity interest in a managed care organization would constitute grounds for the imposition of sanctions under the anti-kickback statute. . . . [Conclusion] we conclude that the Proposed Arrangement . . . poses no more than a minimal risk of fraud and abuse. Accordingly . . . the OIG will not subject the Proposed Agreement to sanctions arising under the anti-kickback statute.

Advisory opinions are considered the best way to ensure that an intended action will not be subject to investigation. They are published on the OIG's website.

Audit Reports

An **audit** is a formal examination or review. Income tax audits are performed to find out whether a person's or a firm's income or expenses were misreported. Similarly, compliance audits judge whether a health care organization's staff members comply with regulations, particularly for correct coding and billing. An audit does not involve reviewing every document. Instead, a representative sample of the whole is studied to reveal whether erroneous or fraudulent behavior exists. For instance, an auditor might make a random selection, such as a percentage of health care claims for a particular date of service, or a targeted selection, such as all claims in a period with a certain procedure code. If the auditor finds indications of a problem on the sample, more documents and more detail are usually reviewed.

Following the audit, the OIG issues **audit reports,** which summarize the department's findings after it has investigated a potentially problematic situation. These reports are also posted to the website. Here is an example.

> The HHS Office of Inspector General has posted an Audit Report to its website. A summary of the report follows . . . Review of the Medicaid Drug Rebate Program, State of Minnesota, Minnesota Department of Human Services, St. Paul, Minnesota . . . The objective of this audit was to evaluate whether the Minnesota Department of Human Services had established adequate accountability and internal controls over the Medicaid drug rebate program. In our opinion, the State had established adequate accountability and internal controls. The financial management system used to provide the necessary information complies with Federal regulations.

Special Fraud Alerts and Advisory Bulletins

OIG Fraud Alerts are issued periodically to inform providers of problematic actions that have come to the OIG's attention. With CMS, the OIG also issues CMS advisory bulletins that alert providers and government-sponsored program beneficiaries of potential problems.

> **Examples** An advisory bulletin explained how Medicare-participating hospitals should handle Medicare and Medicaid patients enrolled in managed care plans when they seek treatment of possible emergency medical conditions.
>
> A Fraud Alert warned physicians to make sure that the home health care and durable medical equipment (DME) they order is medically necessary. It also urged physicians and medical practice staff members to report suspicious activity about false certification of patients' needs for these services. A certificate of medical necessity is needed for Medicare reimbursement of home health services or some types of medical equipment, such as wheelchairs. The alert came after audits showed that some physicians signed certificates of medical necessity without even knowing the patients.

Excluded Parties

If employees, physicians, and contractors have been found guilty of fraud, they may be excluded from work for government programs. An OIG exclusion has national scope and is important to many institutional health care providers because Congress established a civil monetary penalty for institutions that knowingly hire **excluded parties.** The OIG maintains the List of Excluded Individuals/Entities (LEIE), a database that provides the public, health care providers, patients, and others with information abut parties excluded from participation in Medicare, Medicaid, and federal health care programs. As shown in Figure 5-8 on page 134, this list is available on the OIG's website for the exclusion program.

INTERNET RESOURCE
OIG Exclusion Program Home Page
http://oig.hhs.gov/fraud/exclusions/aboutexclusions.html

Although the OIG says that "under the law, covered entities are not subject to civil, administrative, or criminal penalties for innocent errors, or even negligence," decisions about whether there are clear patterns and inadequate internal procedures can be subjective at times, making the line between honest mistakes and fraud very thin. Allied health staff members must avoid any actions that could be perceived as noncompliant.

Corporate Integrity Agreements

The OIG often negotiates compliance obligations with covered entities. The CE agrees to the obligations in exchange for the OIG's agreement not to seek an exclusion of that health care provider or entity from participation in Medicare, Medicaid, and other federal health care programs. Providers who settle these cases often deny that they were liable or that they committed the alleged conduct.

Figure 5-8

OIG Exclusion Program Home Page

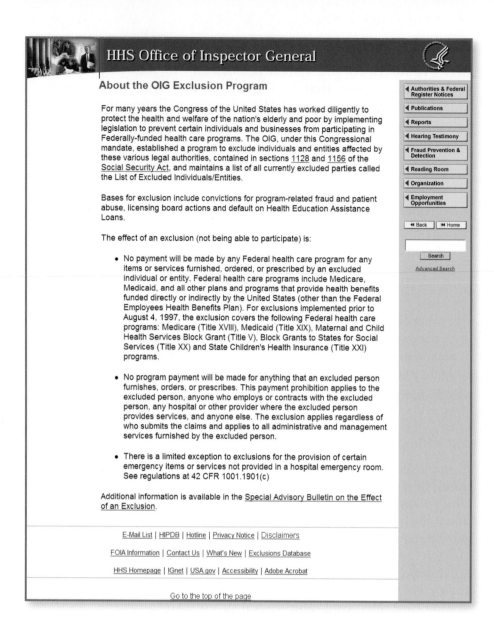

The typical term of a comprehensive **corporate integrity agreement (CIA)** is five years (three years for national project cases). The more comprehensive integrity agreements include requirements to:

> Hire a compliance officer and appoint a compliance committee

> Develop written standards and policies

> Implement a comprehensive employee training program

> Review claims submitted to federal health care programs

> Establish a confidential disclosure program

> Restrict employment of ineligible persons

> Submit a variety of reports to the OIG

While many CIAs have common elements, each agreement addresses, in part, the specific facts of the conduct at issue and is tailored to accord with the existing capabilities of the provider. Integrity agreements often include many of the elements of preexisting voluntary compliance programs.

If the compliance concerns are less serious, the OIG may choose to negotiate a **certification of compliance agreement (CCA)** with health care providers and other entities instead of a comprehensive CIA. Under a CCA, the organization is required to maintain its existing compliance program and agree to certain other compliance procedures.

OIG'S CIVIL MONEY PENALTIES

The OIG is authorized to seek civil money penalties (CMP) and also exclusion from participation in all federal health care programs for a wide variety of activities. For example, penalties and exclusion are sought against any person who:

> Presents claims to a federal health care program that the person knows or should know are for items or services that were not provided as claimed or are false or fraudulent

> Violates the antikickback statute by knowingly and willfully (1) offering or paying remuneration to induce the referral of federal health care program business or (2) soliciting or receiving remuneration in return for the referral of federal health care program business

> Presents a claim that the person knows or should know is for a service for which payment may not be made under the physician self-referral (Stark) law

In addition, the OIG may seek a CMP against any hospital that has negligently violated its obligations under the provisions of the Emergency Medical Treatment and Active Labor Act that require hospitals to:

> Operate an emergency department to provide appropriate medical screening examinations to individuals who present to the hospital and request examination

> Provide stabilizing treatment or an appropriate transfer to any individual who has an emergency medical condition

> Accept appropriate transfers of individuals with emergency medical conditions if the hospital has the appropriate equipment and capabilities under the law

The OIG may also seek a CMP, and in some cases exclusion, against a responsible physician, including an on-call physician, who violates this statute.

The OIG is authorized to seek different amounts of CMPs and assessments based on the type of violation. For example, in a case of false or fraudulent claims, the OIG may seek a penalty of up to $10,000 for each item or service improperly claimed and an assessment of up to three times the amount improperly claimed. In a kickback case, the OIG may seek a penalty of up to $50,000 for each improper act and damages of up to three times the amount of payment at issue, even if some of the payment was for a lawful purpose. As in the case of CMPs

HIPAA ⚠ CAUTION

OIG Statistics

During the first half of federal fiscal year 2007, OIG resolved audit and investigations that led to $2.9 billion in expected recoveries. OIG reported exclusions of 1,278 individuals and entities for fraud or abuse involving federal health care programs and/or their beneficiaries; 209 criminal actions against individuals or entities that engaged in crimes against departmental programs; and 123 civil actions.

1. A hospital and a large multispecialty practice are considering a business merger. They are concerned that they may be targeted for a fraud investigation because they both have Medicare patients. What action would you recommend that they take?

2. A patient of a clinic asked the medical insurance specialist to help her out of a tough financial spot. Her medical insurance authorized her to receive four radiation treatments for her condition, one every thirty-five days. Because she was out of town, she did not schedule her appointment for the last treatment until today, which is one week beyond the approved period. The insurance company will not reimburse the patient for this procedure. She asks the medical insurance specialist to change the date on the record to last Wednesday so that the last treatment will be covered, explaining that no one will be hurt by this change and, anyway, she pays the insurance company plenty.

What type of action is the patient asking the clinic employee to do? How should the employee handle this request?

imposed by the OCR or CMS, entities that are accused of fraudulent activities can request hearings before an administrative law judge (ALJ) and can appeal the judge's decision.

Strategies for Compliance: The Compliance Plan

Given these concerns about HIPAA, fraud, and abuse violations, how does a covered entity protect itself? A wise slogan is that "the best defense is a good offense." For this reason, providers and other health care entities write and implement **compliance plans** to uncover and correct compliance problems. A compliance plan is a process for finding, correcting, and preventing illegal practices. It is a written document prepared by a compliance officer and committee that sets up the steps needed to (1) audit and monitor compliance with government regulations, (2) have policies and procedures that are consistent, (3) provide for ongoing staff training and communication, and (4) respond to and correct errors. The goal of the plan is to promote ethical conduct and establish a culture of compliance in the organization.

The goals of the compliance plan are to:

> Prevent fraud and abuse through a formal process to identify, investigate, fix, and prevent repeat violations relating to reimbursement for health care services

> Ensure compliance with applicable federal, state, and local laws, including employment and environmental laws as well as anti-fraud laws

> Help defend the entity if it is investigated or prosecuted for fraud by substantiating its desire to behave compliantly and thus to reduce any fines or criminal prosecution

Compliance plans cover all areas of government regulation beyond HIPAA, fraud, and abuse, such as Equal Employment Opportunity (EEO) regulations (for example, hiring and promotion policies) and Occupational Safety and Health Administration (OSHA) regulations (for example, fire safety and handling of hazardous materials such as blood-borne pathogens).

GUIDANCE ON COMPLIANCE PLANS

Each of the various types of covered entities has its own range of services, location, and business structure. This means that a good compliance plan for each type will also vary. To offer help in creating compliance plans, the OIG has issued the following **compliance program guidances:**

11/28/05	OIG Compliance Program Guidance for Recipients of PHS Research Awards (Draft)
01/27/05	Supplemental Compliance Program Guidance for Hospitals PDF [Original Compliance Program Guidance for Hospitals PDF (February 23, 1998)]
04/28/03	Final Compliance Program Guidance for Pharmaceutical Manufacturers
03/24/03	Final Compliance Program Guidance for Ambulance Suppliers PDF
09/25/00	Final Compliance Program Guidance for Individual and Small Group Physician Practices
03/16/00	Final Compliance Program Guidance for Nursing Facilities
11/16/99	Final Compliance Program Guidance for Medicare+Choice Organizations
09/30/99	Compliance Program Guidance for Hospices
06/22/99	Compliance Program Guidance for the Durable Medical Equipment Prosthetics, Orthotics, and Supply Industry
11/30/98	Compliance Program Guidance for Third-Party Medical Billing Companies
08/07/98	Compliance Program Guidance for Home Health Agencies
08/24/98	Compliance Program Guidance for Clinical Laboratories

COMPLIANCE TIP

Best Practice: Follow OIG Guidance

Following the OIG's guidance can help in the defense against accusations of HIPAA violations, fraud, and abuse. Having a plan in place shows that efforts are made to understand the rules and to correct errors. This indicates to the OIG that the problems may not add up to a pattern or practice of abuse, but may simply be errors.

INTERNET RESOURCE

Compliance Program Guidance

http://oig.hhs.gov/fraud/complianceguidance.html

The content of each compliance program guidance is not a model plan, because good plans vary for each type of organization, but rather descriptions of what should be covered. The guidances are designed to be used as pointers on how to best create and implement an effective compliance plan.

PARTS OF A COMPLIANCE PLAN

Generally, according to the OIG, voluntary plans should contain seven elements:

1. Written policies and procedures
2. Appointment of a compliance officer and committee
3. Training
4. Communication
5. Auditing and monitoring
6. Disciplinary systems
7. Responding to and correcting errors

WRITTEN POLICIES AND PROCEDURES

The first component of a compliance plan is the organization's written policies and procedures. This material must cover a code of conduct, written compliance policies and procedures, retention of patient medical records and of information systems, and how the policies and procedures are part of employee performance evaluation.

Code of Conduct

A **code of conduct** for the members of the organization rests on basic principles of health care. For example, providers' codes of conduct address these points:

> Act in accordance with all federal, state, and local laws, rules, and regulations.

> Provide high-quality patient care.

> Maintain accurate financial records.

> Recognize that all employees are representatives of the organization.

> Have high ethical standards.

Written Compliance Policies and Procedures

The compliance policies and procedures address many topics, such as employee training, how to report employee noncompliance, and periodic compliance reviews.

Retention of Records and of Information Systems

The compliance plan must cover the retention schedule for patients' medical records as well as for the information systems that house the records.

Performance Evaluations

Compliance plans establish the way in which adherence to the code of conduct, the handling of compliance violations, and attendance at compliance training are elements in employee evaluations.

COMPLIANCE OFFICER AND COMMITTEE

To establish the plan and follow up on its provisions, most organizations appoint a compliance officer who is in charge of the ongoing work. The compliance officer may also be the HIPAA-mandated privacy and/or security officer. A compliance committee is also usually established to oversee the program. The compliance officer and the committee analyze all areas that present risks for out-of-compliance behavior by reviewing:

> Federal and state statutes

> Government-sponsored program regulations (Medicare and Medicaid)

> *Medicare Carriers Manual* and *Coverage Issues Manual*

> Other health plans' regulations

> Current and past years' OIG Work Plans

> OIG Fraud Alerts and audit reports

ONGOING TRAINING

Compliance plans require a training program to keep professional and administrative staff members up to date in pertinent regulatory matters. These training requirements affect managers, supervisors, employees, and business associates. Ongoing training also requires having the current annual updates, such as for HIPAA-mandated code sets, and researching changed regulations. Documentation improvement programs may be part of this training effort.

EFFECTIVE LINES OF COMMUNICATION

The compliance plan describes how employees and business associates can report suspected noncompliant actions. The communications may be by telephone, by e-mail, in face-to-face discussion, or in writing. A separate means of communication, such as a toll-free hotline, is required so that anonymous reporting of noncompliance is possible.

ONGOING AUDITING AND MONITORING

Another major aspect of the compliance plan is auditing and monitoring areas of concern, especially the coding and billing process. The person who is responsible for auditing and monitoring establishes a system for routine internal monitoring and regular compliance checks to ensure adherence to established policies and procedures.

To reduce the chance of an investigation by an enforcing agency and to reduce potential liability when one occurs, most compliance plans require **internal audits** to be conducted regularly. These audits are routine and are performed periodically without a reason to think that a compliance problem exists. They help determine whether financially related activities such as coding and billing are being done appropriately.

COMPLIANCE TIP

Hospital Compliance Serves Two Purposes

Hospital compliance with HIPAA regulations on privacy and security also helps the organization meet the Joint Commission's standards for privacy and security. These two sets of standards are fairly consistent, with HIPAA's being far more detailed.

The following is a list of twenty-five HIPAA compliance points for a covered entity. Are there any points you would modify? Add? Delete?

HIPAA Compliance Checklist for Protected Health Information (PHI)

1. Do staff members discuss PHI among themselves or with patients or family in public areas?
2. Are all staff members trained in office policies before they are given access to PHI material?
3. Is PHI ever announced over intercoms, pagers, or cell phones?
4. Do phone conversations and dictation occur in areas where PHI cannot be overheard?
5. Is transcription completed in an area where PHI cannot be overheard?
6. Are computer monitors positioned away from public areas to avoid observation?
7. Are screens on unattended computers returned to screen saver or the sign-in screen that requires a password?
8. Are documents with PHI that are located in public areas turned face down or concealed to avoid observation by patients or visitors?
9. Are paper records and medical charts stored or filed in such a way as to avoid observation?
10. Has a compliance official been appointed and given resources and training?
11. Is PHI only released by staff member who is specifically trained and authorized to do so?
12. Is the physical access to fax machines and printers limited only to authorized staff?
13. Is PHI discarded in the appropriately secure container or shredded?
14. If answering machines are used, is access to information controlled?
15. If a patient list is utilized that includes patient ID information, is it visible to other patients or unauthorized persons?
16. Are visitors, vendors, maintenance, housekeeping, or other nonpatient care personnel allowed unsupervised into record storage or processing areas?
17. Are patient records or charts stored in a cabinet or room with a lock, and are they routinely secured when no one is in attendance?
18. Has a working team been organized to ensure that compliance is routinely monitored?
19. Do staff members feel comfortable to report misuse of PHI to their supervisor or compliance officer?
20. Do staff members each have a secure password for access to PHI?
21. Are patient charts placed outside patient rooms in a manner that avoids disclosing any PHI?
22. Are all closed records archived in an appropriate manner?
23. Are documents that contain PHI disposed of in secure bins or shredded?
24. Has a staff member been assigned to walk around the office at the end of the day to secure any PHI?
25. Are fax machines monitored throughout the day to ensure that material with PHI is not left available to unauthorized personnel?

Courtesy of Donna Kyle-Brown.

The goal is to uncover problems so that they can be corrected. Internal audits often **benchmark** these activities (compare them against a standard). For example, a billing department of a hospital may be compared to billing statistics from comparable hospitals regarding the average length of stay for certain conditions or surgeries. Another method employed is **triggered reviews,** in which certain events or certain repeated actions cause an audit of noncompliance. These types of events and actions are documented in the compliance plan.

In an **external audit,** an enforcing agency such as the OIG reviews selected records for compliance. Coding linkage, completeness of documentation, and adherence to documentation standards, such as the signing and dating of entries by the responsible health care professional, may all be studied. The accounting records are often reviewed as well.

DISCIPLINARY GUIDELINES AND POLICIES

A compliance plan must include written policies covering appropriate disciplinary actions if employees fail to comply with the organization's rules. Disciplinary actions are usually progressive, meaning that people are given opportunities to correct behavior before being fired. However, the disciplinary guidelines should also list the offenses for which an employee can be fired without progressive discipline. Employees are responsible not only for compliance, but also for detecting noncompliance when routine observation would have provided adequate clues that a problem existed.

The compliance plan should also describe the organization's policies and procedures on requiring background checks to be sure that prospective employees and business associates have not previously been convicted of crimes or excluded from participation in federal programs.

CORRECTIVE ACTION

In this section of the compliance plan, the organization describes the steps to be taken when a report of noncompliance is received. These guidelines state how internal investigations should be conducted, options for corrective action, when to have an outside investigator brought in to conduct an investigation, and when noncompliant actions need to be reported to authorities, such as to CMS, OIG, or law enforcement personnel.

Case Discussion

At the beginning of the chapter, a case relating to sanctions against employees who violated HIPAA law was presented. The problem has surfaced in hospitals and clinics across the nation as they have switched to electronic records. While new technology has made it easier for employees to snoop, it has also made it easier to catch them. Information technology systems track file access—who, when, and how often.

Some health care providers have computer programs that scan for suspicious cases. For example, if a nurse in cardiology reads the medical file of a cancer patient, the computer may send a note asking for an explanation.

Based on the civil and criminal penalties for various HIPAA violations and on the fact that employees of the clinic were informed about the suspension policy, it seems that the punishment is not too harsh. Privacy violations can indeed lead to investigations relating to fraud and abuse, potentially causing financial penalties against the covered entity.

CHAPTER REVIEW

CHAPTER SUMMARY

1. The purpose of the HIPAA final enforcement rule is to reconcile differences in enforcement procedures that had existed between the privacy and the security standards by imposing a single rule that covers all Administrative Simplification provisions.

2. Civil cases involve complaints that individuals have against others based on civil law. Criminal cases involve the enforcement of the criminal code of law by federal, state, and local enforcement agencies.

3. The Office for Civil Rights (OCR) enforces the HIPAA privacy standards in civil cases; the Department of Justice (DOJ) enforces privacy cases that involve criminal activities.

4. The Centers for Medicare and Medicaid Services (CMS) is authorized to enforce the HIPAA security, transactions, code sets, and identifiers standards.

5. In civil cases, the enforcing agency, either OCR or CMS, receives a complaint. Complaints are reviewed to see if they are valid. If they are, the agency conducts an investigation into the nature of the problem. OCR and CMS may coordinate their investigations if the case involves both privacy and nonprivacy aspects. The ideal resolution is voluntary compliance by the covered entity. If that is not possible, civil money penalties (CMP) can be imposed.

6. The Office of Inspector General (OIG) of the Health and Human Services Department (HHS) was directed by the original HIPAA law (Health Insurance Portability and Accountability Act of 1996) to combat fraud and abuse in health insurance and health care delivery; this agency also has the task of detecting health care fraud and abuse and enforcing all laws relating to them. The OIG works with the DOJ under the direction of the U.S. attorney general to prosecute those suspected of medical fraud and abuse.

7. In the health care arena, fraud consists of intentional actions to take financial advantage of another person. Abuse refers to financial gain for the delivery of unnecessary medical services.

8. The Health Care Fraud and Abuse Control Program, part of HIPAA, was enacted to prevent fraud and abuse in health care billing. This law, as well as the Federal False Claims Act and other related laws—including an antikickback statute, the Stark II law, the Sarbanes-Oxley Act, and the Deficit Reduction Act—have been enacted to help control fraudulent billing.

9. The OIG Work Plan lists the year's planned projects for sampling particular types of billing to see if there are problems.

Projects may address any area of health care billing and finance, including physicians, hospitals, long-term care facilities, and other settings. These plans point to the areas on which government investigations will focus. Covered entities study these initiatives and make sure their procedures comply with the existing rules.

10. A compliance plan includes consistent written policies and procedures, appointment of a compliance officer and committee, training plans, communication guidelines, disciplinary systems, ongoing monitoring and auditing of claim preparation, and responding to and correcting errors. Each part of the plan addresses compliance concerns of government and private payers. Having a formal process in place is a sign that the covered entity has made a good-faith effort to achieve compliance.

MATCHING QUESTIONS

Match the key terms with their definitions.

_h_ 1. abuse

_i_ 2. fraud

_a_ 3. Department of Justice (DOJ)

_d_ 4. Office of the Inspector General (OIG)

_g_ 5. Stark II

_c_ 6. relator

_b_ 7. code of conduct

_e_ 8. compliance program guidance

_j_ 9. excluded parties

_f_ 10. Health Care Fraud and Abuse Control Program

a. Federal department that investigates criminal violations of the HIPAA privacy standards

b. Ethical principles contained in the written policies and procedures section of a compliance plan

c. Person who makes the accusation of suspected fraud

d. Federal agency that enforces HIPAA fraud and abuse law

e. OIG publications regarding various health care providers' compliance plans

f. HIPAA program that uncovers and prosecutes fraudulent activities

g. Federal law against physician self-referral

h. Actions that misuse government monies by charging for unnecessary services

i. Billing a federal insurance program for services that were not done

j. Individuals and entities prohibited from participating in government programs

TRUE/FALSE QUESTIONS

Decide whether each statement is true or false.

_F_ **1.** The Department of Justice (DOJ) decides whether to accept civil complaints involving privacy.

_T_ **2.** The Deficit Reduction Act encourages states to pass their own false claims acts.

_T_ **3.** The Office for Civil Rights (OCR) has the authority to subpoena covered entities during an investigation of a privacy violation.

_T_ **4.** The Centers for Medicare and Medicaid Services (CMS) receives complaints about security violations.

_T_ **5.** It is fraudulent to upcode services on health care claims.

_F_ **6.** Because the work was actually done, it is acceptable to change a date of service on a claim for a patient so that the charge is covered.

_T_ **7.** Federal agencies consider a compliance plan a sign of good-faith efforts by a covered entity to comply with HIPAA regulations.

_T_ **8.** Civil money penalties can be required in both privacy and nonprivacy cases.

_F_ **9.** The nonprivacy complaint form is designed to be submitted to the Department of Justice (DOJ).

_F_ **10.** Individuals are authorized to sue for compensation in HIPAA privacy standard violation cases.

MULTIPLE CHOICE QUESTIONS

Select the letter that best completes the statement or answers the question.

1. An OIG Fraud Alert

　a. informs covered entities about upcoming audits

　b. explains the Department of Justice regulations

　c. advises covered entities about compliance problems uncovered by the OIG

　d. provides advice to individuals and business entities

2. The OIG Work Plan describes

　a. planned projects for investigating possible fraud in various billing areas

　b. legislative initiatives under HIPAA

　c. the FBI's investigations

　d. the current cases that are being prosecuted by OIG attorneys

3. Both acts and omissions regarding HIPAA standards may be noncompliant according to the

   a. False Claims Act

   b. Health Care Fraud and Abuse Control Program

   c. HIPAA final enforcement rule

   d. certification of compliance agreement (CIA)

4. Intentionally reporting a service at a higher level than was performed is a clear example of

   a. auditing

   b. a compliance plan

   c. assumption coding

   d. fraud

5. Most complaints regarding violations of the HIPAA privacy standards have been resolved without

   a. legal action

   b. civil money penalties

   c. audit reports

   d. upcoding

6. A compliance plan often includes

   a. work plans, codes of conduct, and advisory opinions

   b. codes of conduct, ongoing training programs, and corrective actions

   c. previous years' code reference manuals, encounter forms, and black box edits

   d. fraud alerts, regulations, and bulletins

7. Benchmarks during an audit help determine

   a. patterns of unsatisfied employees

   b. problems with financially related activities

   c. the need for a toll-free hotline

   d. code of conduct requirements

8. The Office for Civil Rights (OCR) may refer criminal cases to

   a. the Department of Justice (DOJ)

   b. the Office of the Inspector General (OIG)

   c. the Centers for Medicare and Medicaid Services (CMS)

   d. the state attorneys general

9. Civil money penalties cannot exceed what amount for all violations of identical type in a single year?

   a. $5,000

   b. $10,000

   (c.) $25,000

   d. $100,000

10. The greatest criminal penalty can be imposed when the crime is

   (a.) using PHI for profit, gain, or harm

   b. offenses done under false pretenses

   c. knowingly obtaining PHI in violation of HIPAA

   d. none of the above

SHORT ANSWER QUESTIONS

Define the following abbreviations.

1. OIG _Office of Inspector General_
2. FCA _False Claims Act_
3. CMP _Civil Money Penalties_
4. DOJ _Department of Justice_

APPLYING YOUR KNOWLEDGE

HIPAA Cases

Assume that you have the job of receiving HIPAA complaints for the Health and Human Services Department (HHS). Read each case, and decide which department is likely to best handle it. Indicate situations in which you think that more than one department is likely to be involved.

1. An employee of the Department of Veterans Affairs is accused on a complaint form by another employee of stealing vets' names and Social Security numbers from the office computer and selling them.

2. A covered entity sends in a report that one of its employees has left a laptop computer with PHI on it on a bus.

3. A hospital patient complains that she has not been allowed to see the medical record covering her recent hospitalization.

4. A billing service reports that a physician practice for which it works is consistently reporting high-level visits when the encounters appear to be for annual vaccinations.

HIPAA Communications

1. Read the following press release from the OIG and answer the questions that follow.

During this reporting period, OIG resolved two major False Claims Act cases. Its settlement with Tenet Healthcare Corporation, the nation's second largest hospital chain, involves a five-year corporate integrity agreement (CIA) and $900 million to be paid to the agency. The payments include $788 million for extra payments that had been based on inflated charges, $46 million for upcoding DRGs that were unsupported by medical records, and more than $47 million for allegedly paying a kickback to physicians for patient referrals and for billing Medicare for services that were ordered or referred by a physician with whom Tenet had a financial relationship.

Under the CIA, Tenet will implement a comprehensive compliance program and engage independent review organizations to review its DRG claims, outlier payments, physician relationships, and clinical quality management. The CIA also includes unprecedented provisions requiring the Quality, Compliance, and Ethics Committee of Tenet's Board of Directors to review and inform OIG of the effectiveness of Tenet's compliance program.

a. Name the three fraudulent activities that Tenet was accused of.

b. How long is the term of the corporate integrity agreement that Tenet agrees to?

c. According to the press release, are the provisions about the committee of Tenet's board of directors usual?

2. Read the case below, and then answer the questions that follow.

Florida prosecutors indicted two people for charges that include a criminal violation of HIPAA after stolen patient information wound up on bogus Medicare claims, the Department of Justice (DOJ) announced.

Fernando Ferrer, Jr., and Isis Machado face an eight count indictment in the Southern District Court of Florida. Machado allegedly used her position at a Weston, FL, health care clinic, Cleveland Clinic, to download the information of more than 1,000 patients. Machado then allegedly sold the data to Ferrer, her cousin, who used stolen Social Security numbers, names, dates of birth, and Medicare numbers to submit approximately $2.8 million in false Medicare claims.

"Under HIPAA, we expect health care employees to keep our personal information confidential and secure. We will not stand by when this confidentiality is broken and criminals sell and profit from patients' health records," FBI agent Jonathan Solomon said in a DOJ release. The case is the third criminal prosecution of HIPAA.

Ferrer and Machado face HIPAA penalties of 10 years in prison and a $250,000 fine.

    a. Which government department prosecuted the case?

    b. What level of criminal penalty did Ferrer and Machado receive?

RESEARCHING THE INTERNET

1. The Health Care Compliance Association at www.hcca-info.org//AM/Template.cfm?Section=Home offers information and news for health care compliance professionals. Visit this site, and research information on certification.

2. Visit the OIG website at http://oig.hhs.gov.

    a. Click "What's New." Select a recent audit, and prepare a report summarizing its major points.

    b. Using the search feature, locate the OIG Work Plan for either the current or the coming year. Report on activities that relate to one of the health care settings, such as hospitals.

    c. Locate the home page for Enforcement Actions at the Fraud Detection and Prevention tab, and analyze recent enforcement actions. Were they exclusion, CMP, or other actions?

Appendix A

Professional Resources

CCI
The Medicare Correct Coding Initiative automated edits are online at cms.hhs.gov/NationalCorrectCodInitEd/

CMS
Coverage of the Centers for Medicare and Medicaid Services: Medicare, Medicaid, SCHIP, HIPAA, CLIA topics www.cms.hhs.gov
Medicare Learning Network: cms.hhs.gov/mlngeninfo
Online Medicare manuals: cms.hhs.gov/manuals/IOM
Medicare Physician Fee Schedule: cms.hhs.gov/FeeScheduleGenInfo
Conditions of Participation: cms.hhs.gov/CFCsandCOPs
Regulations and guidance: cms.hhs.gov/home/regsguidance.asp

HCPCS
General information on HCPCS
www.cms.hhs.gov/MedHCPCSGenInfo
Annual alphanumeric Healthcare Common Procedure Coding System file
www.cms.hhs.gov/HCPCSReleaseCodeSets
SADMERC
www.palmettogba.com

HIPAA
Home page
www.cms.hhs.gov/hipaageninfo
Questions and Answers on HIPAA Privacy Policies
answers.hhs.gov
www.hhs.gov/hipaafaq/

HIPAA Privacy Rule
"Standards for Privacy of Individually Identifiable Health Information; Final Rule." 45 CFR Parts 160 and 164. *Federal Register 65*, no. 250 (2000).
www.hhs.gov/ocr/hipaa/finalreg.html

Office for Civil Rights (HHS OCR)
OCR Privacy Website
www.hhs.gov/ocr/hipaa
Filing complaints
www.hhs.gov/ocr/privacyhowtofile.htm

Subscribe to OCR-Privacy-list listserv
http://list.nih.gov/cgi-bin/wa?SUBED1=ocr-privacy-list&A;=1

ICD

NCHS (National Center for Health Statistics) posts the ICD-9-CM addenda and guidelines
www.cdc.gov/nchs/datawh/ftpserv/ftpicd9/ftpicd9.htm#guidelines

WHO The International Statistical Classification of Diseases and Related Health Problems, tenth revision is posted on the World Health Organization site
www.who.int/whosis/icd10/

ICD-9-CM addenda
www.cms.hhs.gov/ICD9ProviderDiagnosticCodes
ICD-9-CM Official Guidelines for Coding and Reporting
www.cdc.gov/nchs/datawh/ftpserv/ftpicd9/ftpicd9.htm

NIST

The National Institute for Standards and Technology provides information and recommendations on security issues.
www.nist.gov

NUBC

The National Uniform Billing Committee develops and maintains a standardized data set for use by institutional providers to transmit claim and encounter information. This group is in charge of the 837I and the CMS-1450 (UB 04) claim formats.
www.nubc.org

NUCC

The National Uniform Claim Committee develops and maintains a standardized data set for use by the non-institutional health care community to transmit claim and encounter information. This group is in charge of the 837P and the CMS-1500 claim formats.
www.nucc.org

OCR

The Office of Civil Rights of the HHS enforces the HIPAA Privacy Rule; Privacy Fact Sheets are online at
www.hhs.gov/ocr/hipaa

OIG

The Office of Inspector General of the HHA home page links to fraud and abuse, advisory opinions, exclusion list, and other topics
www.oig.hhs.gov
Model compliance programs are found at
oig.hhs.gov/fraud/complianceguidance.html

TRICARE AND CHAMPVA

General TRICARE information
www.tricare.osd.mil

CHAMPVA Overview
www.military.com/benefits/veterans-health-care/**champva**-overview

WPC

Washington Publishing Company is the link for HIPAA Transaction and Code Sets implementation guides. It also assists several organizations in the maintenance and distribution of HIPAA-related code lists that are external to the X12 family of standards:

- Provider Taxonomy Codes

- Claim Adjustment Reason Codes

- Claim Status Codes

- Claim Status Category Codes

- Health Care Services Decision Reason Codes

- Insurance Business Process Application Error Codes

- Remittance Remark Codes
  www.wpc-edi.com

Glossary

A

270/271 Eligibility for a Health Plan Inquiry/Response 270 and 271 are the ASC X12N eligibility inquiry and response transactions, respectively. This is a way for providers to determine if a patient is covered and how much of the fees are the patient's responsibility.

276/277 Health Care Claim Status Inquiry/Response The ASC X12N claim status request and response transactions. 276 is the inquiry from the provider asking the status of a claim and 277 is the response from the health plan. 277 can also be sent from a health plan asking for more information.

278 Referral Authorization Inquiry/ Response The ASC X12N request for services review and response. It is used to determine pre-certification and referral authorization.

820 Health Plan Premium Payments The ASC X12N transaction standard for payroll deductions and other group premium payments available for use between employers and health plans.

834 Health Plan Enrollment and Disenrollment The ASC X12N benefit enrollment and maintenance transaction. It covers who is or is not eligible for a group health plan.

835 Health Care Payment and Remittance Advice The ASC X12N payment and remittance advice transaction. The first part is the actual payment and the second part explains how the health plan arrived at the amount.

837 Health Care Claims or Equivalent Encounter Information/Coordination of Benefits The ASC X12N professional, institutional, and dental claim transactions (each with its own separate Implementation Guide). The first claim transaction is for primary insurance and the second is for any secondary insurance.

997 Functional Acknowledgment A message commonly used although not a HIPAA standard. It is sent from receivers to the senders of the transaction to tell them the transaction has been received without any transmission errors.

abuse Action that improperly uses another person's or entity's resources.

accounting of disclosures A report that tells a patient to whom his or her health information has been disclosed.

Acknowledgment of Receipt of Notice of Privacy Practices A form signed by patients indicating they have received a copy of a health care provider's notice of privacy practices.

ACS X12 Accredited Standards Committee X12, Insurance Subcommittee (ASC X12N) The ANSI-accredited standards development organization, and one of the six Designated Standards Maintenance Organizations (DSMO). It created and maintains the administrative and financial transactions standards adopted under HIPAA for all health plans, clearinghouses, and providers who use electronic transactions. ASC X12N does not develop claims standards used in retail pharmacies.

addressable implementation specifications Guidelines that must be addressed by a covered entity (CE) or the CE must document why it did not do so.

administrative code sets Code sets used in a general business situation for items, such as zip codes, rather than a medical condition or service. Under HIPAA, these are sometimes referred to as non-clinical or non-medical code sets. *See also* medical code sets.

administrative law judge (ALJ) A judge who presides over complaint hearing in HHS and makes determinations of penalties.

Administrative Simplification (A/S) The part of HIPAA that gives HHS the authority to mandate the use of standards for the electronic exchange of health care data; to specify what medical and administrative code sets should be used; to require the use of national identification systems for health care patients, providers, payers (or plans), and employers (or sponsors); and to specify the standards to protect the security and privacy of ePHI. This is Title II.

administrative standards Under HIPAA, the standards for security to protect electronic protected health information (ePHI) that a covered entity must perform.

advisory opinion Legal opinions issued by the OIG or CMS upon request of an individual, such as a physician, or a legal entity, such as a hospital, that formally presents a situation and asks whether the way they intend to handle it is fraudulent.

amendment A correction of a finalized entry in a medical record that has been identified as incorrect.

antivirus software Software that scans a computer system for viruses and attempts to remove the virus and, in some cases, fix any problems that the virus has caused.

audit A formal examination or review, such as a review to see if an entity is complying with regulations.

audit reports The formal report issued after an audit, especially one issued by the OIG.

authentication The process of verifying that a person who seeks access to electronic protected health information (ePHI) is in fact the person he or she claims to be.

authorization The process of determining whether a particular user (or a computer system) has the right to carry out a certain activity, such as reading a file or running a program. Also, a form giving written permission for something, such as the release of medical information.

availability The process of ensuring that the systems responsible for delivering, storing, and processing data are accessible when needed, by those who need them under both routine and emergency circumstances.

B

backup procedure   The activity of copying files to another medium (such as tape, disk, CD, or online backup service) so that they will be preserved in case the originals are no longer available.

benchmark   To compare something against a standard, such as an activity looked at in an audit that is compared against a HIPAA standard.

business associate (BA)   A person or organization that performs a function or activity on behalf of a covered entity, but is not part of the covered entity itself. Business associates, such as law firms and accountants must adhere to HIPAA standards in order to do business with a covered entity.

C

Centers for Medicare and Medicaid Services (CMS)   (formerly known as HCFA) The division of Health and Human Services responsible for health care. CMS is responsible for Medicare and parts of Medicaid. CMS maintains specifications for various certifications and authorizations used by the Medicare and Medicaid programs. CMS also maintains various code sets.

certification of compliance agreement (CCA)   An agreement between the OIG and a health care entity in which the OIG negotiates a compliance agreement for infractions that are not considered serious.

civil money penalties (CMP)   Financial penalties imposed by the OIG for a wide variety of conduct.

civil violation   A violation of civil law as opposed to a violation of criminal law.

claim adjustment reason codes (RC)   A national administrative code set that identifies the reasons for any differences, or adjustments, between the original provider charge for a claim or service and the payer's payment for it.

claim attachment   Supplemental health information needed to support a particular health care claim. There are a variety of hardcopy forms or electronic records needed to process a claim in addition to the claim itself.

claim status category codes   A national administrative code set that indicates the general category of the status of health care claims. Used in communication from the payer to the provider.

claim status codes   A national administrative code set that further details the status of health care claims in addition to claim status category codes.

clearinghouse   (also called Health Care Clearinghouse) A company that handles electronic transactions for providers, such as submitting claims using HIPAA formats and may also manage electronic medical records.

code of conduct   A written document created by a health care provider for members of its organization based on the basic principles of health care and HIPAA rules and regulations.

code set   Alphabetic and/or numeric representations for data. Medical code sets are systems of medical terms that are required for HIPAA transactions. Administrative (nonmedical) code sets, such as ZIP codes, are also used in HIPAA transactions.

compliance plan   Written plan created by a health care provider or health plan that includes: written policies and procedures; appointment of a compliance officer and committee; a code of conduct; training plans; effective lines of communication; ongoing auditing and monitoring; disciplinary guidelines and policies; and corrective action for errors.

compliance program guidance   Guidance issued by the OIG for the preparation of compliance plans.

confidentiality   The assurance that electronic protected health information (EPHI) is shared only among authorized individuals or organizations.

confidentiality notice   A statement on all faxes and e-mails instructing the receiver to destroy the materials and contact the sender immediately, in the event that the transmission reached him/her in error.

Consolidated Omnibus Budget Reconciliation Act (COBRA)   An amendment to Title I of HIPAA that gives employees the right to continue health coverage as a private payer for a limited period of time once they leave a job.

corporate integrity agreement (CIA)   A negotiated agreement between the OIG and a covered entity (CE) in which the CE agrees to certain obligations in return for the OIG's agreement not to exclude the CE from participation in federal health care programs.

covered entity (CE)   A health plan, a health care clearinghouse, or a health care provider who transmits any health information in electronic form in connection with a HIPAA transaction.

creditable coverage   Insurance coverage under a group health plan, a health plan, or the Medicaid program know as SCHIP. This coverage is taken into account when an employee joins a new health plan.

criminal violation   A violation of criminal law as opposed to a violation of civil law.

cryptography   The protection of information by transforming it into an unreadable format before it is distributed. To read a message, the recipient must have a key that deciphers the information.

Current Dental Terminology (CDT)   HIPAA-mandated code set for procedures performed in a dental office.

Current Procedural Terminology (CPT)   HIPAA-mandated procedural code set developed, owned, and maintained by the American Medical Association.

D

Deficit Reduction Act (DRA) of 2005   A federal law designed to reduce fraudulent claims. It encourages states to pass their own false claims acts.

degaussing   A method for disposal of electronic media with personal health information in which a strong magnetic field is applied to fully erase the data.

de-identified health information   Medical data from which individual identifiers have been removed.

Department of Health and Human Services (HHS)   The federal department that administers federal programs covering public health and welfare.

Department of Justice (DOJ)   The federal government's main law enforcement division.

designated record set (DRS)   a group of medical records. For providers, it includes medical and billing records but not other items, such as lab tests. For a health plan, the designated record set includes enrollment, payment, claim decisions, and medical management systems of the plan.

Designated Standard Maintenance Organization (DSMO)   An organization that has been designated by the

Secretary of HHS to perform those activities necessary to support the use of a HIPAA standard. Such organizations make technical corrections to an implementation specification, expand a code set, or recommend other modifications to keep the standard current.

digital certificates   Digital files that certify the identity of an individual or institution seeking access to computer-based information.

direct provider   A health care provider who has a direct treatment relationship with a patient, such as a physician or therapist. *See also* indirect provider.

disclosure   release or divulgence of information by a health care entity to persons or organizations outside of that entity. Rule is in HIPAA Part II.

documentation   Systematic, logical, and consistent recording of a patient's health status—history, examinations, tests, results of treatments, and observations—in chronological order in a patient medical record.

E

e-discovery   The process of gathering information from digital sources for use in legal proceedings.

EIN (Employer Identifier Number)   The 10-digit federal tax number for employers, issued by the Internal Revenue Service, and adopted under HIPAA as the Standard Unique Employer Identifier.

electronic data interchange (EDI)   The electronic exchange of information between computers, especially the exchange of health information among physicians and insurance companies.

electronic medical record (EMR)   or electronic health record (EHR or EMR) Collection of health information that is immediately electronically accessible by authorized users.

encounter   Visit between a patient and a medical professional.

encryption   The process of encoding electronic information in cryptography.

ePHI   PHI that is stored or transmitted in electronic form.

excluded parties   Employees, physicians, and contractors who have been found guilty of fraud, and are excluded from work for government programs.

external audit   A formal examination in which an agency, such as the OIG, selects certain records for review.

F

False Claims Act (FCA)   A federal law that prohibits submitting a fraudulent claim or making a false statement or representation in connection with a claim.

Federal Employees Health Benefits (FEHB) program   The program that provides medical insurance coverage to the more than 8 million federal employees, retirees, and their families. Administered by the federal government's Office of Personnel Management (OPM).

Federal Register   A publication of the Office of the Federal Register (OFR), which is responsible for publishing federal laws, presidential documents, admistrative regulations and notices, and descriptions of federal organizations, programs, and activities.

firewall   A security device that examines traffic entering and leaving a network, and determines (based on a set of user-defined rules) whether to forward it toward its destination.

fraud   Intentional deceptive act to obtain a benefit.

G

group health plan   Medical insurance offered to employees and payed for in part or in full by an employer.

H

Health Care Common Procedure Code System (HCPCS)   A classification system for medical procedures, services, and supplies. It was set up to give providers a coding system that describes specific products, supplies, and services patients receive that are not in CPT.

Health Care Fraud and Abuse Control Program   A HIPAA program designed to uncover and prosecute fraud and abuse.

health insurance reform   *See* Title I.

Health Insurance Portability and Accountability Act (HIPAA) of 1996   The federal legislation covering rules regarding the health care industry, specifically how it is administered and the

rights of patients in regard to health care coverage and privacy.

health plan   Any individual or group plan that provides or pays for medical care.

HIPAA Electronic Health Care Transactions and Code Sets (TCS)   HIPAA standards governing the electronic exchange of health information using standard formats and standard code sets.

HIPAA Employer Identifier   HIPAA standards that mandate using certain identifying numbers for employers that sponsor health plans and for providers.

HIPAA final enforcement rule   HIPAA rule that reconciles differences in enforcement procedures that had existed between the privacy and the security standards. This single rule covers all administrative simplification provisions.

HIPAA privacy rule   Law that regulates the use and disclosure of patients' protected health information (PHI).

HIPAA security rule   Security standards that require appropriate administrative, physical, and technical safeguards to protect the privacy of protected health information against unintended disclosure through breach of security.

hybrid record   Medical record that is made up of both electronic and paper documents.

I

identity theft   The criminal use of another person's personal information to take on that person's identity.

ICD-9-CM   *International Classification of Diseases, Ninth Revision, Clinical Modification* Mandatory code set used by the United States. It provides rules for selecting and sequencing diagnosis codes in both the inpatient and the outpatient environments.

ICD-10-CM   International *Classification of Diseases, Tenth Revision, Clinical Modification*, published in 1990 and expected to be made mandatory for the United States.

implementation guide   The official source of detailed technical information on how the HIPAA administrative and financial transactions are to be implemented.

implementation specifications   Under HIPAA, the specific instructions for implementing a standard. This is in Part II, Implementation Guide.

incidental use and disclosure The release of protected health information (PHI) that happens as a result of correct use and disclosure.

indirect provider A health care provider is a person or business that has an indirect treatment relationship with the patient, such as a laboratory. *See also* direct provider.

integrity The certainty that the electronic information is not changed in any way during storage or transmission, and that it is authentic, complete, and can be relied upon to be sufficiently accurate for its purpose.

internal audit Routine audits that a covered entity performs regularly by itself as part of its compliance plan.

L

legacy numbers The identifying numbers that were in use before the National Provider Identifier (NPI) system.

M

malware Any program that harms information systems; often brought into organizations through email attachments or programs that are downloaded from the Internet.

medical code sets Codes that are used for a medical condition or treatment. These code sets are usually maintained by professional societies and public health organizations. *See also* administrative code sets.

medical record Progress notes, reports, and other clinical materials relating to a patient and maintained by a health care provider.

medical standards of care State-specified performance measures for the delivery of health care by medical professionals.

minimum necessary standard Principle that individually identifiable health information should be disclosed only to the extent needed to support the purpose of the disclosure.

N

National Drug Codes (NDC) A code set maintained by the Food and Drug Administration (FDA) that classifies drugs and biologicals. It was originally required for use in the ASC X12N standards, but is now required for use only in retail pharmacies. Hospitals and physicians are not required to use this code set.

National Plan and Provider Enumeration System (NPPES) A system set up by HHS which processes applications for NPIs, assigns them, and then stores the data and identifying numbers for both health plans and providers.

National Provider Identifier (NPI) Under HIPAA, a system for uniquely identifying all providers of health care services, supplies, and equipment.

network security The practice of protecting and preserving resources and information on a network.

Notice of Privacy Practices (NPP) A document stating the privacy policies and procedures of a covered entity (CE).

Notice of Proposed Rule-Making (NPRM) A document that describes and explains rules that the Federal Government proposes to adopt at some future date. Interested parties are invited to submit comments, which may then be used in developing a final regulation.

O

Office for Civil Rights (OCR) The division of Health and Human Services responsible for enforcing the HIPAA privacy rules. Privacy is considered a civil right.

Office of the Inspector General (OIG) Federal agency that investigates and prosecutes fraud against government health care programs such as Medicare.

OIG Fraud Alert Alerts issued periodically to inform providers of problematic actions that have come to the OIG's attention.

OIG Work Plan A list of the year's projects that the OIG will be working on in areas that the government is investigating. This list is given to covered entities (CEs) so that they can make sure they are in compliance.

P

password A string of numbers and/or characters that are required to log into a system, used as a means of preventing unauthorized users from gaining access to information on a computer or network.

physical standards Under HIPAA, standards that require covered entities to implement policies and procedures that limit unauthorized physical access to electronic information systems such as computers as well as the facilities where the ePHI is stored. including portable/mobile media devices

place of service (POS) Under HIPAA administrative code that indicates where medical services were provided.

preemption The rule that HIPAA rules supersede state laws except when HIPAA deems a state law necessary to prevent fraud and abuse or when the state law is more restrictive than the HIPAA rule.

protected health information (PHI) The HIPAA terminology for individually identifiable health information in any medium, except such information maintained in education records covered by the Family Educational Rights and Privacy Act (FERPA) and employment records.

protocol A set of rules governing the format of messages that are to be exchanged electronically either within a network or between two parties.

provider People or businesses that furnish, bill, or are paid for health care in the normal course of business. Under HIPAA, a covered provider is one who submits electronic administrative and financial transactions.

Q

qui tam Meaning "who as much;" refers to the whistle blowers in whistle blower cases.

R

relator A person who makes an accusation of suspected fraud.

release of information (ROI) Release of information (ROI) of a patient's information.

remittance advice (RA) An electronic message that explains how a payer arrived at benefits.

remittance advice remark codes (REM) Remark codes maintained by CMS and used by payers to explain why payments differ from billed amounts.

required implementation specifications Under HIPAA, specifications that must be performed by covered entities. These specifications include administrative, physical, and technical standards.

risk analysis The process of creating policies and procedures to protect electronic protected health information (ePHI).

risk management The establishment of policies and procedures that reduce the risk of breaches of security.

role-based authorization A structure set up by most covered entities (CEs) in which access is based on the individual's title and/or job function, so that only people who need information can see it.

S

sanction policy Under HIPAA, a key specification that requires covered entities (CEs) to set up a policy that states the consequences for violations of security policies and procedures by employees, agents, and contractors.

security incidents Defined in HIPAA as "the attempted or successful unauthorized access, use, disclosure, modification, or destruction of information or interference with system operations in an information system."

small health plan Under HIPAA, a health plan with annual revenue of 5 million dollars or less. It is in Part II.

Stark II Federal law that prohibits self-interested referrals, or referrals in which the entity referring has a financial interest or may receive a kickback.

subpoena An order by a court requiring a party to appear and testify.

subpoena *duces tecum* A subpoena that also includes the requirement to bring certain documents.

T

taxonomy codes A ten-digit number that stands for a physician's medical specialty. The codes are published by the Washington Publishing Company.

technical standards Defined in HIPAA as "the technology and the policy and procedures for its use that protect ePHI and control access to it."

Title I The portion of the HIPAA law concerned with health insurance reform. The main purpose of Title I is to ensure the continuation of health coverage when employees change jobs. It also entitles people who leave a job to continue their health insurance coverage as a private payer for a limited period of time under COBRA.

Title II The portion of the HIPAA law known as administrative simplification. The rules in this section cover administrative, financial, and case management policies and procedures. It contains strict requirements for the uniform transfer of electronic health data and covers rules of patient confidentiality.

transaction One electronic exchange in EDI, specifically under HIPAA, the exchange of information between two parties involved in financial or administrative activities related to health care. It is in Part II.

treatment, payment, and health care operations (TPO) Under HIPAA, the rule that patients' protected health information may be shared without authorization for the purposes of treatment, payment, and operations.

triggered reviews An audit or review triggered by certain events or certain repeated actions indicating noncompliance.

U

unique user identification Under HIPAA, an implementation specification that requires every individual in the workplace to have his or her own unique name and/or number for access to the computer system.

upcoding Use of a procedure code that provides a higher payment than the code for the service actually provided.

W

workstation An electronic computing device such as a laptop or desktop computer and electronic media stored in its immediate area.

Index

277 Health Care Claim Status Response, 93, 94, 96, 104–105
278 Referral Certification and Authorization, 93, 94, 95

U

Unique user identification, 75
Upcoding, 131

V

Viruses, computer
antivirus software, 67

defined, 64
malicious mobile code, 64

W

Washington Publishing Company (WPC), 104
Women's Health and Cancer Rights Act, 6
Workers' compensation
exemption from HIPAA standards, 13, 33, 42
First Report of Injury, 94
Workflow clearance procedures, 71
Workforce security, 69

Workgroup for Electronic Data Interchange (WEDI), 17
Workstations
security of, 73
use of, 72–73
World Health Organization (WHO), 98, 100
Worms, 64

X

X12 implementation guidelines, 17